Discovery Design

"This book is an absolute gem. It provides an informative and practical step-by-step account to guide healthcare improvers through the design process, and would be an asset to both fledgling practitioners and seasoned professionals alike. It is now my new "go-to" resource and I wouldn't be without it."

— Tim Riding

Associate Director, Centre for Perfect Care
Mersey Care NHS Foundation Trust

"Discovery Design challenges us to rethink how we approach improvement in healthcare. As an improvement scientist, I've personally seen how the techniques outlined in this book provide clarity from complexity, connect leadership to the experience of clinicians, staff nurses and patients, and deliver creative and effective solutions from our patient care units to the organization as a whole. I encourage all healthcare professionals to consider integrating the tools and processes of human centered design that are so well articulated in Discovery Design."

— Paul Sharek, MD, MPH

Professor of Pediatrics (Hospital Medicine),
Stanford School of Medicine
Medical Director Center for Quality
and Clinical Effectiveness
Chief Clinical Patient Safety Officer,
Lucile Packard Children's Hospital

"What an amazing handbook! So many clinicians need this. I'm making this required reading for my students."

— Cosima Gretton MD

Product Manager, Karius
Technology Entrepreneurship Teaching Fellow
University College London, UK

"Healthcare is starving for good design as one of the most complex and dangerous systems known to man. Alas creative thinking is socialized out of us young, leaving behind the belief that the dream of patient centered systems and safe care is helplessly dependent on armies of PHDs, professional designers, and large financial infusions. Channeling the spirit of the most inspiring innovators and innovations in history, this handbook provides a tool kit that once again proves imagination, inspiration and achievement doesn't require more than a formidable will and a game plan. This is the game plan!"

— Lisa Scafidi

Director of Risk Management
Children's National Health Network

"Academic medical institutions around the world now prioritize design principles in training future clinician-innovators. From identifying and articulating an unmet clinical need to navigating the complexities of stakeholder priorities and an ever-evolving set of constraints, Discovery Design provides a scalable framework that is vital to those looking to generate measurable impact in health and medical domains."

— Farzad Azimpour, MD

Director of Health, IDEO
Adjunct Professor, Stanford University School of Medicine
Assistant Director of Design,
Stanford Byers Center for Biodesign

"Discovery Design provides a framework for designing care that works; by emphasizing the needs of people: the patient, the care-team, and the organization. More than that—it's an actionable guide for improvers looking to successfully navigate the unique challenges and minefield of health care improvement."

— David Pickham, PhD RN FAHA

Executive Director of Research, Patient Care Services,
Stanford Health Care
Assistant Clinical Professor, Medicine -
Primary Care and Population Health
Stanford University School of Medicine

"As a medical student, I'm constantly thinking of ways to improve the healthcare experience for patients but don't have an organized framework for studying problems and implementing change. Discovery Design combines quantitative research with the nuanced methodology of design and guidance to innovate and implement thoughtfully! This guide is a must have for all healthcare innovators, experienced and new alike."

— Jennifer Loretta Liao

MD Candidate, Class of 2019
The George Washington School of Medicine & Health Sciences

"Few design domains are as complex as healthcare, but likewise, few are as rewarding to inspire change in. The pragmatic experience and design thinking passion captured in this handbook will help teams discover a path forward, powered with empathy and insight, navigating the realities of working inside health care systems."

— Katja Battarbee

Principal XD Researcher, Innovation Practices Intuit

"So often, we hear about the successful outcome without understanding the process behind it. This will enable many health system stakeholders to apply this methodology to their own improvement efforts."

— Claudia Amar, RN, BScN, MHA

Program Manager, Healthcare Delivery Systems
Clinical Excellence Research Center (CERC)
Stanford University

"While the phrase "patient-centered" has become a cliché, in efforts to make care more effective, health care organizations often struggle to engage with the people most responsible for health outcomes - the care team and the patients themselves! Discovery Design offers an approach to designing systems of care that patients and clinicians actually want and need. Our program could not have been successful over the past 6 years without first learning to better "empathize" with the people we were trying to serve. I can no longer imagine seeking to transform the care system and not starting the journey in a design mode. Bravo!"

— Alan Glaseroff MD

Co-Founder, Stanford Coordinated Care
Clinical Professor of Medicine
Stanford University

"The Discovery Design process works. From the first project meeting, we could tell this approach was different and a welcome complement to other improvement methodologies. It provided a sensitivity that helped articulate the needs at the frontline in new ways, and nurse engagement continued to increase as we cultivated solutions together. We will certainly utilize this method again and I commend it to anyone seeking to spark empowered change!"

— Shannon Feehan MSN, RN, CPN

Patient Care Manager, PCU 374
Stanford Children's Health

"Discovery Design meets us right where we're at in patient safety and quality. It's a companion that provides new tools for innovation and improvement, and the hard-won wisdom needed to do it! Healthcare is so often immune to change. Leveraging empathy and evidence, this could be the cure. It's become a staple in our practice."

— Tim Bowers, MS CIC CPHQ

Director of Quality & Patient Safety - Ambulatory
Inspira Health Network

“If design thinking has always baffled you, this book is the key to unlock its potential. As health care designers, we believe the best ideas burst forth when everyone is trusted and respected for the expertise they bring, and when the voices of end-users like patients and caregivers are brought to the surface. At Medicine X, we call this way of seeing the world, Everyone Included™. It’s a theme that runs down the very center of Discovery Design. This playbook is what anyone who wants to improve health care needs to generate the best ideas and see them transform practice in patient care settings.”

— Larry Chu, MD

Professor of Anesthesiology, Perioperative and Pain Medicine
Executive Director, Stanford Medicine X Health Care Innovation Program
Stanford University School of Medicine

Discovery Design

Design Thinking for Healthcare Improvement

Disclaimer

This handbook is for educational purposes only and is intended to be an introduction to various strategies that may be used to improve healthcare systems. It is not intended to apply to any particular fact situation, provide specific advice, or guarantee any particular result can be achieved in any specific matter. Reliance on any information herein is solely to the risk of the reader. The handbook is not a substitute for professional consultation and we recommend you always seek the advice of a qualified professional with any questions you may have regarding strategies described.

Stanford Medicine | The Risk Authority

riskmanagement@stanfordhealthcare.org

www.med.stanford.edu

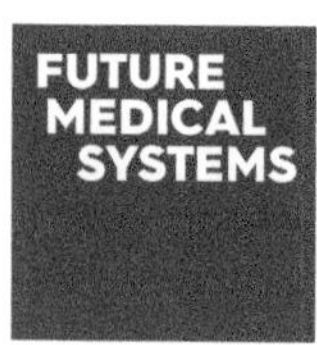

Future Medical Systems, LLC.

www.futuremedicalsystems.com

hello@futuremedicalsystems.com

Credits

Editors

Barry Katz
Professor, California College of the Arts
Consulting Professor, Stanford University
Fellow, IDEO

Jeff Driver
Chief Risk Officer,
The Risk Authority, Stanford Medicine

Simon Mawer
Director, Innovence Lab,
The Risk Authority, Stanford Medicine

Design Advisor

Resonance Partners
http://www.resonancepartne.rs
info@resonancepartne.rs

Production Manager

Christopher Moyer
Creative Director, Hard Luck Creative

Authors

Simon Mawer
Director, Innovence Lab, The Risk Authority
Stanford Medicine

Svava María Atladóttir
Senior Partner, Future Medical Systems, LLC

Kara Harrington
Senior Partner, Future Medical Systems, LLC

Rob Lister
Senior Partner, Future Medical Systems, LLC

Lucie Richter
Senior Partner, Future Medical Systems, LLC

Future Medical Systems, LLC

Future Medical Systems is a unique design and development consultancy dedicated to creating meaningful healthcare experiences. We are passionate about uncovering the underlying needs of healthcare professionals, patients, caregivers, and administrative staff, and using this insight to drive service, product, and workflow innovation. Our process is a systems-led approach that results in reduced risk, better care and better outcomes, all at lower cost. We create these results by:

> **Delivering tangible, human-centered design**
> We design medical products and services based on in-depth insight into people and their underlying needs. We deliver communications, interfaces, and service design direction to improve care delivery processes, workflows, medical devices, environments, and consumer health and wellness experiences.
>
> **Crafting meaningful experiences for the entire journey**
> We guide organizations in implementing new care models and health interventions that are both impactful and sustainable for care providers, patients, caregivers, and families. Through our focus on people, we create thoughtful systemic approaches that meet the needs of multiple stakeholder groups, developing journeys that span teams and touchpoints.
>
> **Building improvement cultures**
> Often the greatest opportunities for improvement lie in finding better ways for an organization to support its patients, staff, clinicians, and leadership. We work with executives and leadership to develop strategies and roadmaps that transform teams and organizations, creating alignment across leadership and care teams, sparking creativity, and implementing new models of care.

Future Medical Systems arose from the experiences of four IDEO designers who saw the need for a customized approach to the theory and practice of Design Thinking, one that reflected the rigor and constraints of the healthcare ecosystem. We are delighted to share the fruit of this journey and of our wonderful partnership with The Innovence Lab at The Risk Authority, in Discovery Design.

Innovence Lab at The Risk Authority

Innovence Lab is an initiative of The Risk Authority, an award-winning risk management and design consultancy serving the Stanford University medical institution.

Our beginnings
Innovence Lab was created in response to the recognition that traditional healthcare risk management, improvement, and design approaches have not delivered on their promise of safer and more effective care. In 2013, stakeholders from across the Stanford University healthcare ecosystem came together and imagined a capability that could "move the needle" by blending the creative methods of design, the rigor of improvement science, the tools of business, and a deep understanding of what it takes to create change in healthcare organizations.

Leveraging evidence and innovation, Innovence Lab emerged with the goal of generating human-centered and data-validated solutions to the most important risk and safety challenges facing patients and healthcare providers today. It has become a space for physicians, nurses, patients, data-scientists, designers, improvers, risk managers, and administrators to come together and reimagine systems of care, creating impact that can be expressed in human and financial terms.

Our work
Grounded in data and inspired by people, our work touches every domain of healthcare risk. We have developed solutions for improving teamwork in the operating room, supporting patients after medical mistakes, preventing adverse drug events, improving clinical workflows, reducing employee injuries, supporting clinician wellness, and developing system-wide risk and quality improvement strategies.

Our invitation
Discovery Design represents the culmination of our learning to date, forging a holistic approach that we have seen create impact both at home and at healthcare organizations we've worked with across the USA and UK.

Acknowledgements

It takes a community...

Discovery Design was made possible by an exceptional community of thinkers and doers who generously lent us their ideas, perspectives, examples, and suggestions.

We are so grateful for the generosity of thought and feedback from our colleagues in the healthcare design, risk management, research, and improvement communities: To Katja Battarbee and Hillary Carey, who helped us articulate steps through the synthesis process. To Aaron Sklaar, Nina Serpiello, Meg Lee Weir, Deuce Cruse, Leslie Witt, Judy Lee Haworth, Candice Tillit, Annie Valdes, Kristian Simsarian, and Gretchen Wustrack, for their thoughtful support and feedback over the years and in particular for this handbook. To Claudia Amar, Dr. Kyra Bobinet, Dr. Jeff Bleich, Caroline Bell, Kevin Burson, Monica Ferreira, Mara Brazer, Bob Cady, Dr. Cosima Gretton, Mat Hornberger, Mary Beth Kelly, Tami Kelly, Jennifer Loretta Liao, Samantha Broom, and Giselle Mawer, for adding their perspectives and feedback. To our partners Grace Li, Monisha Perkash, Charles Wang, Andrew Chang, Eric Chehab, Dr. Ann D Lindsay, and Dr. Alan M Glaseroff, who helped us share stories and examples. Additional thanks to Tad Simons, Don Westwood, Stacey Chang, and Abbe Don, who helped us find this path and gave us opportunities to hone our skills.

Thanks to David Pickham, Dr. Paul Sharek, and Beatrice Podtschaske for refining our thinking on the convergence of design, quality improvement, human factors engineering, and medical research. To Kim Pardini-Kiely for being a believer, mentor, and a champion. To Dr. Larry Chu and the Medicine X team, for inspiring empathy-driven healthcare innovation that includes all of its stakeholders. They also kindly lent us a variety of images to include in this handbook. To Christopher Moyer, for his masterful production support in the final phases—you took us over the line. To Veronique Grenon and Randall Smith for helping us articulate ways in which healthcare innovators can make the financial business case for their initiatives.

To Jeff Driver, who lit the spark that became Discovery Design. Thank you for giving us the courage and space to explore, create, and evolve an approach that is already creating real impact for patients, providers, and healthcare organizations across the globe. This project could not have taken flight without your vision and support.

To our partners from Stanford Health Care and Stanford Children's Health, Kelly Johnson, Cassie Bergero, Krisa Elgin, Shannon Feehan, Jenna Oslan, the nurses and patients of PCU 374, Mary Song and our Patient & Family Partner Program project teams, Dr. Loren Risken, and Dr. Paul Sharek: you have shaped and shared Discovery Design with us through all the twists and turns of healthcare innovation. It's been a sacred privilege to share the journey with you! To Tim Bowers, Tim Riding, and Lisa Scafidi for lending your perspectives and inspiration from the trenches.

To Soren DeOrlow, for your partnership over these past three years and the ways in which you have shaped our thinking about patient-centered design. You've brought passion, strategy, and tangibility to these ideas, lending credibility and inspiring creativity. We would also like to acknowledge and thank our current and former colleagues, mentors, and friends at IDEO for their inspiration, generosity, and support over many years.

Our humble thanks to Barry Katz. Your mentorship, encouragement, advice, and steady hand has guided us through the unknown! You brought your wisdom, precision, passion, and sensibility to shaping and giving expression to our ideas. We feel honored and privileged to have had the opportunity to partner with you.

Finally, to our spouses, families, and friends who patiently and lovingly supported us through many late nights generating, iterating and refining this work, and especially when the going got tough. We could not have done this without your generous and unfaltering support.

Table of Contents

Foreword XVII

Preface XVIII

Introduction 1

Phase 1: Scope 15

Phase 2: Prepare 55

Phase 3: Discover 91

Phase 4: Synthesize 131

Phase 5: Generate 167

Phase 6: Prototype 193

Phase 7: Pilot 223

Phase 8: Spread 265

Conclusion 285

Bibliography and Resources 293

Foreword

Few of us imagined that the launch of the Hasso Plattner Institute of Design at Stanford University—the scrappy initiative known better by its nickname, the "d.school"—would in a few short years achieve worldwide notoriety for the concepts of Design Thinking. After all, we had been teaching human-centered design at Stanford for more than 50 years before starting the d.school. What began as an experiment in design education for the masses has evolved into a movement to adopt this innovation process in companies, organizations, and institutions of every sort.

Underlying the philosophy of Design Thinking is the premise that change should neither be pushed by technology nor pulled by market opportunities, but driven by the real needs of real people. Much of our work has been devoted to developing the human-centered tools that will enable us to reach these deeper insights. It is gratifying that this innovation strategy has caught the attention of progressive businesses across all industries.

Almost all industries, that is. The clinics, hospitals, and medical schools that comprise the healthcare system have—with good reason—been notably slow to adopt methodologies that may seem overly subjective, experimental, or simply more suited to product-oriented enterprises. For this reason, we should all welcome Discovery Design, the first attempt to adapt the methods and principles of Design Thinking to the world of healthcare organizations.

The authors of this handbook are not red-shoelaced "designers," but experienced healthcare professionals who are steeped in the world of medicine, familiar with its technical, regulatory, and cultural intricacies, and committed to the data-driven, evidence-based foundations upon which it is built. At the same time, they bring to their work, a deep immersion in the principles of human-centered design and have achieved a remarkable synthesis of these two fields of practice.

We believe that everyone deserves access to the latest medical technology and innovative, cost-effective healthcare. Above all, we believe in placing the patient's needs—physical and mental—at the center of the healthcare experience. Discovery Design represents this new approach, adapting the proven methodology of Design Thinking to the complex requirements of healthcare, poised to be the next frontier of innovation. Discovery Design will lead the way.

William Burnett
Executive Director, Stanford University Design Program

Preface

"To study the phenomena of disease without books is to sail an uncharted sea, while to study books without patients is not to go to sea at all."

—William Osler

We believe that risk management has the potential to transform health systems—that it is rich with untapped potential, but that it is often too slow to identify and mitigate risks effectively. We can feel adrift at sea and without steady winds to take us to port.

But as we embrace new thinking, the promise of risk management bursts forth. Leveraging data and machine learning, we can ride the waves of insight. Leveraging design, we can chart a new course. And leveraging decision analysis, we can reach the promised shores—healthcare systems that support and protect our providers, patients, caregivers, and families, providing care that doesn't falter.

Inspired by this promise, our team set out on a path to strengthen our risk management methods. We recognized the need for a new model for mitigating risks, one based on evidence *and* empathy; one centered on the real needs of the people involved. We developed a strategic partnership with Future Medical Systems, leveraging their expertise in design and our own in the processes of healthcare risk, improvement, and operations.

Today, the fruit of that partnership is Discovery Design, the handbook you are holding. In Discovery Design, you will find a credible companion for applying data-driven and creative approaches for tackling the most important risks facing your healthcare organization. It will be a compass as you navigate the tumultuous seas in which we work and serve.

Discovery Design will speak to you, and we hope that you will talk back! We have designed it to be used in any way that suits you—write in it, photocopy it, fill it up with sticky notes. Take it with you to your project meetings. Choose the methods that will be most useful to you and your team. Let it inform and augment your process of discovery.

We will walk you step-by-step through the design process as we apply it in the hospital environment. We have organized these steps into eight phases, each with several steps, many examples, and spaces for generating your own ideas. You will learn to adopt new ways of thinking and discover new capabilities for yourself and your team.

Our hope is that when you walk away from having completed your first Discovery Design project, that you will feel energized, empowered, and excited to pick it up again for your next adventure.

Simon Mawer

Svava María Atladóttir

Kara Harrington

Rob Lister

Lucie Richter

Introduction

"Everyone designs who devises courses of action aimed at changing existing situations into preferred ones."
—Herbert Simon

Welcome to Discovery Design

The world of healthcare can be a harsh environment for new ideas and new thinking. The stakes are high, and people are working under enormous pressure. The culture is understandably cautious about considering new directions without strong evidence of their value. There is inescapable complexity, not to mention the realities of business, markets, and brands. And, not least, we are dealing with layers of accrued conventions that often compensate for inefficient or outdated practices rather than tackle them head on.

But it is also a world rich with opportunity and ripe for new ways of thinking about the challenges facing healthcare professionals today. Discovery Design is a creative and empathy-driven approach that takes its inspiration from the latest thinking in healthcare improvement and incorporates creative problem-solving strategies drawn from the field of design. Grounded in theory but oriented toward practice, the goal of Discovery Design is to help healthcare improvers reduce risk and improve outcomes for patients, clinicians, and organizations alike.

Who is this handbook for?

Discovery Design offers a human-centered approach to solving complex problems from the perspective of the people who are affected by them. It can be used as a guide for anyone who is committed to creating positive change: clinicians and clinical team leaders; risk management, process excellence, and quality improvement specialists; suppliers and administrators; product managers in the medical device and pharmaceutical industry; and physicians, nurses, and patient advocates. We believe that with the right tools, anyone can be a leader of change.

What is in the handbook?

This handbook introduces the creative approaches designers bring to problem solving but with specific reference to the challenges faced by healthcare professionals. Readers will be guided through the stages of the design process, from embarking on a program of change to scaling the outcomes throughout an organization. These include:

- Using data-driven and design-centered approaches to gain a rich understanding of the challenges facing clinicians, administrators, patients, and patients' families.
- Translating needs into insights and insights into solutions.
- Piloting ideas in real-world settings.
- Using systems design and management tools to evaluate change concepts.
- Scaling new ideas and spreading them across an institution.

The processes outlined in this Handbook will help healthcare professionals generate new ideas that address real needs, launch practical solutions that can be implemented in existing systems and workflows, and monitor and continuously improve them. Whether in large-scale initiatives or smaller ones, the goal in every Discovery Design project is to deliver maximum value for patients, clinicians, and the health system at large.

Who created this handbook?

This Handbook was developed by the Innovence Lab at The Risk Authority, which serves as a hub for value-driven innovation in healthcare risk management for Stanford Medicine and its clients worldwide, in partnership with Future Medical Systems, a consultancy that applies design methodologies to the healthcare field. The methods and examples included here are derived from our professional experience and draw upon a wide range of sources.*

* See the Bibliography for attributions and acknowledgments.

Thinking about design

Any time we work to solve problems, improve systems, or enhance processes, we are designing. In this sense, we are all designers, even if we don't always do it mindfully or according to a formal methodology. There is a difference, however, between problem solving that may be sincere, conscientious, and intuitive, and the rigorous methodologies used by design professionals.

Over the course of a century designers have developed a body of practices that have been applied to everything from kitchen appliances to precision medical devices. In recent years, under the banner of "Design Thinking," their techniques have been leveraged not just to products, but to organizations, systems, and processes.

Whereas design practice has its roots in consumer product development, Design Thinking is now being used to inspire innovative solutions across a wide range of industries. It typically begins with an intensive research phase intended to understand the challenges faced by the people who will be served, foster deep empathy with them, and generate ideas that are uniquely fitted to their situations. Design Thinking has proven particularly helpful when there is not a clear understanding of the problem, let alone a single right answer.

By placing people at the forefront of efforts to solve complex, systemic problems, Design Thinking is uniquely effective in aligning diverse stakeholders and giving each of them—physicians, patients, or front-line staff—a voice.

Leading organizations including Mayo Clinic, Kaiser Permanente, Sutter Health, Robert Wood Johnson Foundation, and Stanford University School of Medicine have applied elements of Design Thinking to the challenges of healthcare improvement. We believe that it is time to codify what we have learned and to adapt it to the specific requirements of healthcare organizations.

Discovery Design can be thought of as Design Thinking adapted to the specific context of healthcare. Borrowing client-centered techniques found in a range of fields—the social sciences, product design, human factors and ergonomics, organizational psychology, and risk management—Discovery Design provides healthcare professionals with a guide for innovation at the organizational scale. It provides healthcare innovators with the tools to discover underlying issues that may be obscured by existing data or established practices.

In contrast to the top-down approach familiar to most medical professionals—in which data is evaluated, a solution is proposed, and a new solution deployed—we introduce a human-centered approach that begins with the people at the "sharp-end" of care and works upward through the entire chain of stakeholders. By incorporating both quantitative and qualitative data and encouraging both creative and analytical thinking, Discovery Design provides a richer, more holistic understanding of the people and contexts in which they work.

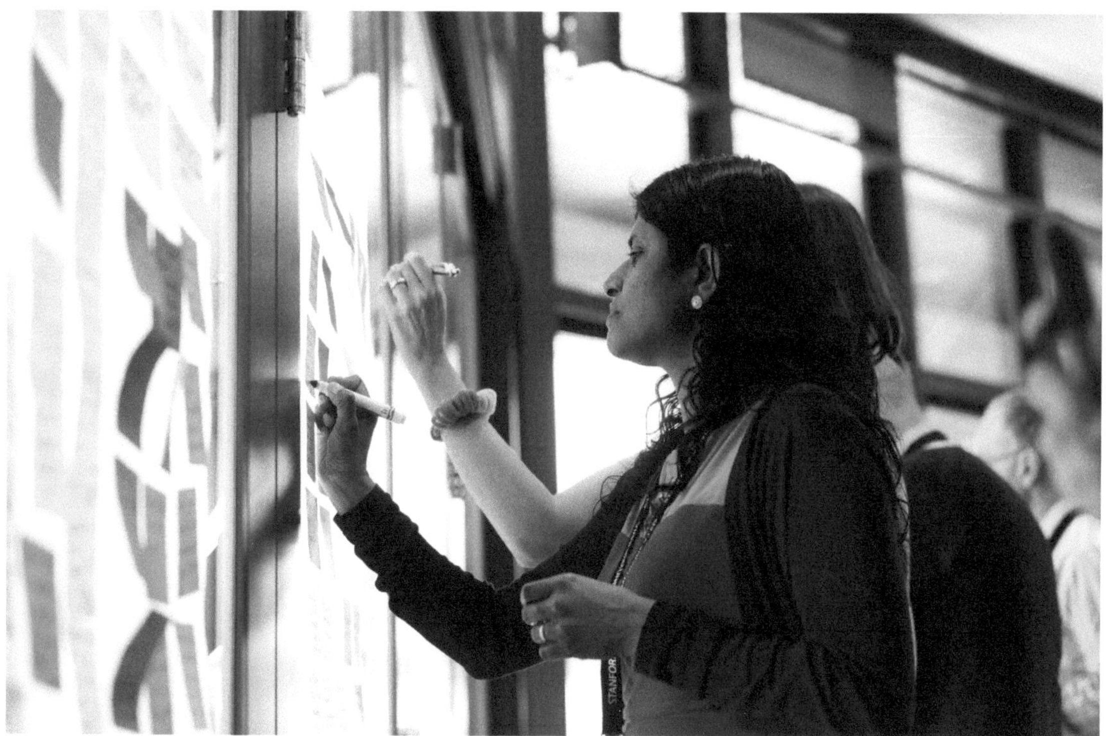

Management science and business strategy

Discovery Design is responsive to the concerns of the boardroom as well as the operating room. Discovery Design understands that new ideas must be framed within viable business models if they are to compete with existing priorities and resource constraints. Borrowing tools from risk management, business strategy, and decision analysis, it ensures that new initiatives are grounded in organizational priorities and are able to demonstrate their value for people and for the bottom line.

PDSA, Lean Six-Sigma, and EBP

Discovery Design adds a new dimension not only to Design Thinking, but also to two of the foundational methodologies of modern improvement practice. The first is the "Plan-Do-Study-Act" (PDSA) cycle developed by W. Edwards Deming and adapted by the Institute for Healthcare Improvement to clinical environments. The second is Lean Six-Sigma, inspired by the management practices of Japanese manufacturing organizations. Discovery Design builds on these frameworks by integrating the empathic and creative sensibilities of design.

Discovery Design is also consistent with Evidence-Based Practice (EBP). Discovery Design, which is human-centered, exploratory, and qualitative, offers an essential complement to evidence-based, data-driven exploration. Designers search for the opportunities that are likely to be most productive and where numerical evaluation may not yet be a reliable guide. These will eventually be rendered over for quantitative assessment through empirical testing and other rigorous evaluation.

Discovery Design owes a great debt to theories and practices that have proven their value in real-world environments. Integrated into existing processes, Discovery Design can help distill the universe of possibilities and establish new directions in modern healthcare.

Avoiding the three-year cycle

We have observed that many improvement projects follow a familiar three-year cycle:

In Year One a new solution is presented with great fanfare and achieves some early success. In Year Two the program hits some bumps but is held together by a new team that has been told to "make it work." In Year Three a new priority emerges—amid another round of fanfare—and the old one fades into memory.

Efforts to improve healthcare fall victim to this cycle for a number of reasons, among them:

1. Mischaracterizing the problem: "It was executed perfectly, but solved the wrong problem."
2. Lack of buy-in: "They made this big change without even talking to us..."
3. Insufficient resources: "We're in a budget crunch; we knew it was a good idea, but there wasn't money to invest in the program."
4. Failure to prove impact: "We knew it was working—but they were looking at these other data. We didn't get the chance to measure that."
5. Failing to sustain change: "It ran out of steam and never went anywhere."
6. Getting lost in the weeds: "We got stuck fighting fires."

Discovery Design was created to help innovators avoid these common pitfalls and overcome what developmental psychologist Robert Kegan identified as "immunity to change"—a pervasive mindset in large organizations that predisposes them to preserve the status quo.

> "We can't solve problems by using the same kind of thinking we used when we created them."
>
> —Albert Einstein

The advantages of the Discovery Design approach can be summarized as follows:

- In understanding the problem space, Discovery Design looks at the larger system context and the relationships among different stakeholders.
- Discovery Design generates a wide range of possible solutions before narrowing the field through iterative testing at low resolution in simulated use.
- By virtue of its focus on searching out underlying needs, Discovery Design defines the qualities of an ideal solution and then measures a broad range of solutions against those qualities.
- Discovery Design engages multiple stakeholders. This ensures that all parties feel included in the creative process, as well as enhances alignment on any solutions that are generated.

The designer's mindset

Although we describe a specific set of tools, Discovery Design is as much a mindset as a methodology. As an approach to innovation, it is characterized by principles as well as processes, values as well as data, inspiration as well as analysis. For designers, these mindsets are the foundations upon which effective initiatives are built. Discovery Designers tend to be optimistic, empathic, inclusive, experimental, curious, and action-oriented:

Optimistic

The designer's mindset is fundamentally optimistic and focused on what could be; without the confidence that we can achieve positive results, what is the incentive to dive in and take action? A room full of design thinkers will resonate with "What if…?" and "How might we…?" rather than "That will never work," or, "We tried that last year."

Empathic

Rather than frame their approach in terms of technological capabilities or institutional realities, we approach problems from the perspective of the people who experience them. We listen to what they say (and don't say), observe what they do (and don't do), and elevate their "local" expertise.

Inclusive

To unlock the power of collaboration, the best ideas must be permitted to rise to the surface, irrespective of their source. We identify opportunities collectively, we conceive and refine them in concert, we prototype solutions and test them with people in real-world situations, and everyone shares credit and assumes responsibility. Discovery Designers are more likely to speak in terms of "we" and "us" than of "I" and "me."

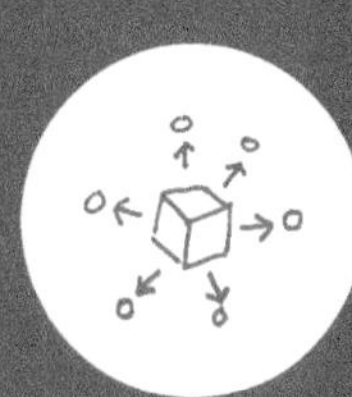

Experimental

We emphasize the freedom to explore many ideas with the expectation that the eventual solution will be the richer and more sustainable. The experimental mindset is comfortable with ambiguity and trusts in the process to open up ideas to life in a repeating learning cycle.

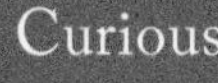

Curious

The most powerful insights often come from the most unexpected sources, so we draw our inspirations from wherever we can find them—and not just from the field of healthcare! Creative people need to explore many paths and peer around many corners. In the words of legendary humanitarian Linus Pauling, "If you want to have good ideas, you must have many ideas."

Action-oriented

Designers are always experimenting with ways to give form to ideas: "Show, don't tell" is their common refrain. More than white papers and reports, designers will communicate ideas by drawing pictures, constructing storyboards, building models, and finding imaginative ways of simulating experiences. Systems live in the real world, and the best way to test whether a solution might work is to make it visible and tangible.

Getting help

This handbook aims to support a range of scales of effort, from grassroots and guerilla teams to those supported by a mature and permanent team. If your aim is to ramp up quickly, you may consider bringing in a consultant team to provide you with a solid and successful first step. A team of experienced consultants can provide a very powerful source of support and learning.

Some factors to consider when hiring consultants:

- Looking in: Require them to conduct a preliminary research exercise in order to understand the perspective of your organization.
- Ongoing support: They should be willing to make a key member of the team available to you for some period of time after the main term of the project.
- Relevant experience: Are they trained, experienced designers? Can they personally point to examples of insights that delivered value they uncovered?
- Delivery: Can they show examples of systemic, multi-stakeholder concepts that have been implemented in the healthcare environment?
- Engagement: Do they see engaging on the ground with the staff of your institution as part of their contribution?
- Scale: Do they have experience with your scale of organization, big or small?

Before you begin...

Change is hard, and changing complex health systems can be even harder! People move on, technologies change, priorities shift, and auditors might arrive tomorrow—and regulators the day after. Moreover, every project is as unique as the organization to which it is directed. It's natural to feel a sense of trepidation about launching a major new initiative, so as you prepare to embark, we offer some practical wisdom:

First, start small, gather quick wins, and let momentum build over time. For most people, undertaking change initiatives is not their full-time job, so be sure to carve out time in your calendar to block other priorities out and release you to focus on the work.

Second, recognize that you are likely to find yourself under-resourced and under-supported. Be confident that you can do much more with much less than you think. Try to plan ahead and leverage attention when you have it.

Third, accept that people may be apprehensive about your efforts. Despite your best intentions, healthcare professionals may be wary based on their past experiences, competing priorities, or a multitude of other factors. Be respectful towards those who at first seem cool, use empathy, and try to get to the bottom of their concerns.

Fourth, keep your expectations realistic and look for ways to leverage your successes. Demonstrate that progress is being made. Everything will take longer than you think, so strategize accordingly.

Fifth, understand that although efforts to improve are never final, it's important to have a clear endpoint to your project. Make sure you, your team, and your stakeholders recognize key milestones and are aligned on the stopping point.

Finally, appreciate that significant projects demand personal investment. Be kind to yourself, sleep well, enjoy your team, and take time for moments of inspiration—an evening out, a good book, a weekend adventure. Nurture your creative soul, as it is from there that everything else flows.

The eight phases of Discovery Design

Discovery Design flows through eight broadly defined phases, starting with how to select a project, and ending with how to scale and spread your solutions. Each phase has its own steps, which will guide and propel your project forward.

Phase 1: Scope
Explore the data and the organization. Determine what to work on.

Phase 2: Prepare
Gather your team and plan the project.

Phase 3: Discover
Conduct research in order to understand the problem space.

Phase 4: Synthesize
Interpret learning and define opportunities.

Phase 5: Generate
Brainstorm and conceive new ideas.

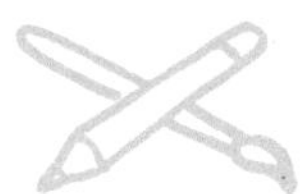

Phase 6: Prototype
Select promising ideas to develop and test.

Phase 7: Pilot
Pilot your idea in successive stages. Prove its value by measuring impact.

Phase 8: Spread
Make the business case, secure support, and launch your solution into the world!

“The designer has a dream that goes beyond what exists, rather than just trying to fix what exists. The designer wants to create a solution that fits in a deeper situational or social sense.”

—David Kelley

Discovery Design can breathe new life into existing practices and can help implement healthcare programs that are preventative and predictive, rather than simply reactive. In this handbook, risk and quality managers will find ways to improve patient safety by redesigning processes mindfully and collaboratively; clinicians will better mediate between the institutional constraints under which they operate and the subjective needs of their patients; and staff will be made to feel that their expertise is valued and understood.

You are ready to begin. We invite you to Discover Design!

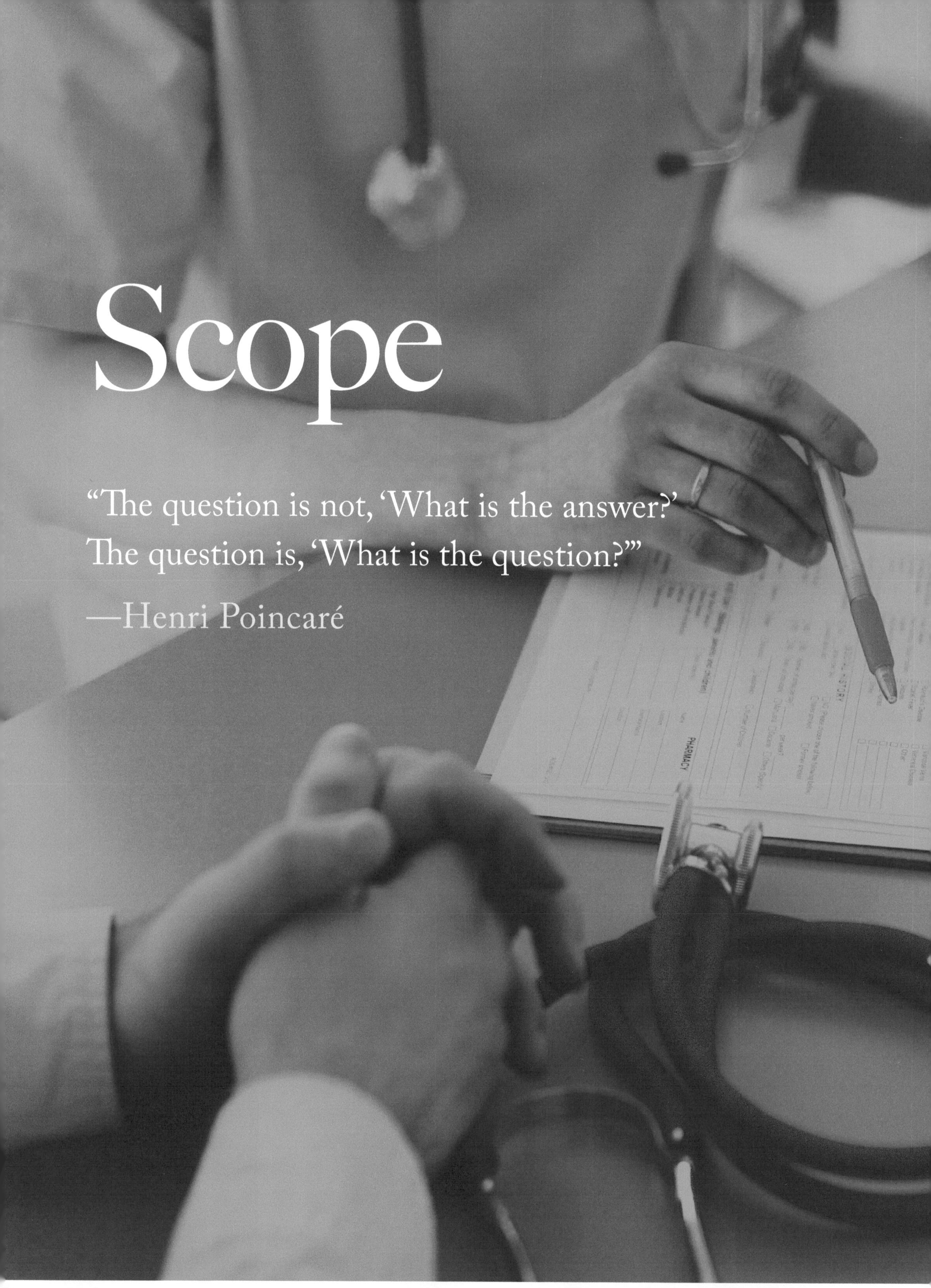

Scope

"The question is not, 'What is the answer?'
The question is, 'What is the question?'"

—Henri Poincaré

The process of selecting a project will reveal many problems in your organization that are worthy of your efforts. Choosing the right one, and defining it correctly, is the single biggest factor that will determine your success—so spend whatever time it takes to get it right. A well-defined project will serve as a beacon, a roadmap, and a call to action. It should be flexible enough to allow for mid-course corrections, yet solid enough to bring a team back into alignment when paths begin to diverge.

The goal of this phase of the Discovery Design process is to help you choose the problem to work on. You will then refine the project scope, seek the necessary buy-in, and secure approval to get started. By the end of Phase 1 you will have defined your challenge and be ready to begin building the team that will tackle it.

Process steps

Step 1-1 Explore the data

What do the numbers say?

Step 1-2 Explore the system

What does the organization say?

Step 1-3 Evaluate the potential return

Explore the upside.

Step 1-4 Select your challenge

Synthesize your inputs.

Step 1-5 Refine the scope

Set your parameters.

Step 1-6 Validate your decisions

Check your decision quality.

Step 1-7 Secure a mandate

Get the necessary buy-in.

Step 1-1 Explore the data

What do the numbers say?

In order to make the case for strong executive support for your improvement efforts, first look at the data sources. What do they tell you about the most important issues affecting your organization? Then, look to the organization to determine the opportunities that are ripe for design.

Statistically, risk touches on every aspect of the healthcare system, from clinical outcomes, to financial, legal, regulatory and social effects.
At The Risk Authority, we use the Innovence Pulse system to crunch data from a very wide range of sources, which helps direct us toward areas that may be ripe for improvement, as well as establish a baseline state from which to measure impact.

Data sources you may wish to consider include:

1. Risk data

- Insurance claims
- Insurance exposures (numbers of visits, doctors, and surgeries per year)
- Actuarial reports
- Insurance premiums

2. Quality data

- Incident reports
- Unsolicited patient complaints
- Root cause analyses
- Peer review
- Provider rosters
- Patient satisfaction surveys

3. Patient data

- Electronic medical records
- Billing data
- Telemetric data
- Device data (including smartphone apps and fitness or wellness trackers)

4. Strategic data

- Sociodemographic new surveys
- Physicians and provider wellness programs
- Employee engagement
- Interviews
- Social media statistics

Considerations for interpreting data

Bear in mind that while data is essential to making a case for why something matters (and for measuring the impact of possible solutions), interpretations can be misleading for a variety of reasons.

First, behavioral dynamics may mask statistical irregularities. In an informal analysis of data from the incident report database of one of our clients, we noticed that the majority of incidents were reported by one functional group about errors attributed to another group. This may have been accurate, or it may reflect a tendency to protect one's own team. Members of one nursing team admitted that if they saw "one of their own" making a mistake, they'd be more likely to have a quiet word with that person than fill out an incident report.

Second, the specificity of data can mask embedded assumptions in the construction of the data set. For example, the literature on medication administration errors indicates that interruptions from the external environment are a significant contributing factor (Westbook, 2010). That may be true, but these "distractions" may be a symptom of something else: an unsupportive environment, misaligned workflows, a troubled relationship among stakeholders, fatigue, possibly even a lack of motivation. "Distractions," in other words, are not a root cause in themselves.

Third, we must be mindful of any inherent weaknesses contained within particular sets of data. What kinds of events might be absent from the data? What biases might come from the data-capture method itself? Research has found that voluntary incident reports capture only 2% to 6% of clinical safety events (Sharek, 2006; Wolf et al., 2008), perhaps due to incident reporting systems design, cultural factors, or varying understandings of what events should be reported. Considering this, how might we appropriately interpret what the incident data is telling us?

"The temptation to form premature theories upon insufficient data is the bane of our profession."

—Sherlock Holmes

Fourth, it is important to recognize that an event does not necessarily tell us anything about the human motivations underlying that event. In a 1991 study published in The Lancet, "Why Do People Sue Doctors?" researchers found that the most important drivers in filing a lawsuit following an adverse healthcare outcome were how the patients and families were treated by the care team after the event (Vincent, et al.). In other words, we cannot simply assume that the safety events themselves are the problem.

Finally, it is important to be mindful of the timing of the events that give rise to the data. Claims and litigation data, for example, often derive from events that occurred 6 months to 4 years in the past (or in the UK, up to 10 years). Taken alone, this can pose challenges to those seeking actionable information as to where they should focus their efforts. Other data sets, by contrast, can be more forward-looking and predictive of where serious risk, quality, cost, service, and safety challenges may materialize in the future. Patient satisfaction, employee engagement, turnover, staff utilization, strategic plans, and legislative or regulatory reform can all provide clues as to where efforts should be directed.

Explore the data

When you are ready to explore the data, use the following workflow:

1. Identify and interrogate multiple data sources across the organization that might reveal opportunities for a project.

2. Interrogate the data sources, looking for limitations, hidden assumptions, and biases. Seek the help of experts where you can!

    - Where did the data come from? Can you trust the source?

    - Why was it collected? The purpose for collecting the data can greatly affect the conclusions that may be drawn from it. As the saying goes, "You get what you measure." How do other people use this data? If your purpose is atypical, be wary about the conclusions you might draw from it.

- How was it collected? Actively or passively? Automatically or by hand? Could the manner of collection skew the results?
- How representative is the data? Which populations were included? How many data points are there? Is it statistically significant? When was it collected? Is the data still relevant?
- How was it presented? The way data is visualized can mask its conclusions. Ensure you evaluate disparate data sources on equal footing.
- Do the numbers make sense? Don't throw away your intuition. If the numbers don't "feel right," find out why.
- What else might be missing? What hidden biases or limitations might there be?
- Do the conclusions make sense? Put yourself in the shoes of someone looking to disprove your conclusions. Anticipate counterarguments. Make the data—not you—work hard to make its arguments. Above all else, do not oversell the conclusions the data is capable of providing.

3. Look for patterns within and across data sets. Overlay different sets of information and look for themes that might reveal an area for investigation.

   If you started with liability claims, how do these relate to incident reports? How about to patient satisfaction and complaints? How do they relate to key quality indicators or employee engagement? Are there points of connection or correlation? Be wary of the extent to which you can make conclusions.

   Often times, the most we say is that "[x data source] has indicated a [y] trend over the past 3 years. At the same time, [z data source] showed [w] over the same time. We do not know whether these are related, but this might hint at an area for further investigation."

4. Complement your analysis with a review of the literature. With the benefit of large data sets, researchers are often able to report on correlations that may not show up in your analysis. Do you see any of these dynamics reflected in your data? Does the literature provide a basis for making inferences about what the data says?

5. What problem spaces seem most promising? Identify several potential areas of focus. Choose at least 3-5 significantly different alternate directions to explore.

The project selection process does not end here. Detailed and accurate data is essential to any modern healthcare environment, but they have limitations and should be handled appropriately. As we move through Discovery Design, we will dig deeper to explore the human, systemic, and technological drivers, experiences, and stories behind the data. Our efforts will reveal rich insights into opportunities as well as obstacles.

As we move into the next section, we'll extend our analysis further, exploring the dynamics within the healthcare organization to see which challenges might represent the ripest opportunities for design.

Step 1-2 Explore the System

What does the organization say?

A nuanced, integrated view of the data will help you narrow your scope to a handful of candidates for a project. Our second lens, then, is the system view: We study the dynamics of the organization to see which opportunities have the greatest chance of bearing fruit. Marrying data with a systems view will likely bring forward one or two directions that feel the most promising.

In Discovery Design, we try to answer the following questions before committing ourselves to a project:

Is the problem a priority?

While the data points to a problem that might be important to you, it is important to establish that the problem matters to the organization.

For systemic change to occur, it will need the support of executive leadership: What is the story leaders will want to be able to tell at the end of this project? Is there a problem they want to solve, or a data point they want to affect? What do they want key stakeholders to say about the project once it is complete?

The support of leadership is essential, insufficient. Any wide-ranging change initiative will need the support of the key stakeholders who will need to be engaged throughout the life of the project.

Will it garner frontline engagement?

Discovery Design calls for deep engagement with people at the frontline of care, and works best when they are involved in the process. Nothing is more difficult than introducing a new project to busy people who do not view your effort as adding value to them. Tackle something where a single key stakeholder group (doctors, nurses, patients) already feels the pain of the issue. Are they available to take part in your project? Does it resonate with them? Would a solution be perceived as a benefit by the people for whom it is intended? If possible, involve members of these groups in the scoping effort.

Do you have strong partners?

Do you have adequate executive sponsorship for the project? Will the relevant decision makers ensure you have a clear path as you move through the project from launch to implementation? Will they remain active through the life of the project? Do you have enough cover to let you navigate the difficult political dynamics that will inevitably arise?

Learn from previous endeavors. Are there teams or leaders in your organization who have earned a reputation for collaboration and effectiveness? Are there opportunities to partner with them? Any change is perceived as disruptive by someone. To mitigate the pushback, engage people who are hungry for change and with whom you already have strong personal relationships. Do you have key champions who are motivated to commit time to participating in design activities and have the authority and resources to test them?

Set yourself up for success by exploring partners *before* you launch your project. We were tasked with a project to improve medication workflows. In an exploratory meeting, we brought together physicians, pharmacists, nurses, administrators, and patient advocates to share our initial insights and see who might be interested in partnering with us. Several potential partners came forward and some offered suggestions of other people we should involve. The meeting was invaluable for helping identify where and with whom we should direct our efforts—and places to avoid!

Is it ripe for design?

Some projects are more amenable to design solutions than others. Does yours involve a system of people, where motivations, feelings, and behaviors are relevant? Do people's behaviors not make sense or deviate too far from training or standard operating procedures? Are there multiple stakeholders? Is this a problem where new ideas are desired? Are there multiple possible "right" answers? These are the spaces where Discovery Design thrives.

In healthcare environments, almost everything is regulated. Be sure to understand whether you project needs to be subject to rigorous scientific protocols.

Is it approachable?

Does somebody else have responsibility for solving the problem you are interested in? Is it already being studied? If others are already interested or working on the problem, they might be enthusiastic partners and sources of talent, resources, and energy. On the other hand, you may be viewed as competing or duplicating efforts already underway.

If the problem areas you are looking at seem to be supported by the data and are amenable to design, you are ready to put together a project proposal. However, it may be advantageous to explore the value-creation potential of your project in order to garner sufficient attention and investment to begin.

Step 1-3 Evaluate the potential return

Assess the upside.

Genuine improvements in healthcare will generate value for an organization at many levels: reducing the risks for patient harm, improving the experience of care for both patients and providers, and improving patient care outcomes, cost savings, engagement, reputation, accreditation, hospital rankings, revenues, and staff retention.

A significant challenge with healthcare improvement projects is that they are systemic in nature and often have to compete for time, resources, and attention. In many situations, the organization's existing budget or priorities toward a particular issue, question, problem, or opportunity will provide the necessary mandate and support to proceed. In others, developing a holistic view of the system you are seeking to improve—and not just the discrete events that initially motivated your efforts—can be essential to success.

> "Healthcare ROI encompasses more than money saved or earned; it must take into account both qualitative benefits such as improved patient safety and improved relationships with patients, as well as streamlined clinical operations among others measures."
>
> —Bobbi Brown & Leslie Falk

A formal analysis can be enormously effective for helping you choose a project that has the greatest potential, justify the resources you need for the project, and provide a baseline for measuring results after implementation. Demonstrating the value your efforts will bring to the wider organization—in such areas as operational efficiencies increases in patient satisfaction, and reductions in turnover—is often the best way to capture the active interest of key partners and stakeholders. Here, we present a robust approach to calculating the potential financial return from projects that require a significant investment of resources. It can be scoped up and down as appropriate for your project.

Evaluating the return

By the end of this exercise, you should be able to come up with a concise "elevator pitch" with which to present your project proposal. Here is a template drawn from one of our recent projects you might use as inspiration:

> "We have been considering where to focus our efforts over the coming year in line with our strategic priorities...
>
> Over the past three years, we've had ___ claims, ___ events, and ___ complaints in [clinical area], where our safety and patient satisfaction scores are __% against the benchmark. Our initial analysis has indicated that these issues are costing us between _____ and ______ per year, and are creating risks for patient harm, staff engagement, and disruptions to operations.
>
> Our project will focus on uncovering the source of these problems, develop one or more interventions, and evaluate their impact over time. We believe that if we are able to improve ______ by even ____%, we could retain staff, improve [quality] outcomes, enhance patient satisfaction, and save the organization $______.
>
> To assure maximum success, we would like to ask your support in the following ways: [be specific!]."

To get to this point, we suggest the following approach:

1. Brainstorm costs and benefits

To work out the potential upside of your project, you will need to establish a holistic view of the financial and non-financial implications of the issue you are seeking to address. We do this by brainstorming the various costs and benefits associated with the system that will be impacted by your project. We call these "value drivers."

Remember that easily measurable items may have indirect or otherwise intangible consequences that may not be obvious on the surface. Try to identify as many of these as you can. Be creative and go beyond the things that can easily be measured. As your team will discover, intangibles can drive significant value to your project—or exact significant costs.

For example, the value of reducing false alarms from fall mattress sensors by 15% might seem obvious at first, but on closer analysis, you'll discover that it takes 15 minutes to respond to each alarm (15 minutes of RN time = $). You'll also note that RN satisfaction is impacted by the false alarms, causing a higher attrition rate, increased recruiting and retention costs, among other outcomes. Even when something appears intangible, there may be tangible measures to assess it.

Value drivers you may wish to consider in evaluating new projects include:

- Initial expenditures.
- Ongoing expenditures.
- Time and costs incurred associated with litigation.
- Time and costs incurred in investigating incidents, and conducting root cause analyses and peer reviews.
- Length of stay, equipment costs, personnel costs, and operational efficiencies.
- Costs of non-reimbursable events, such as readmissions within 30 days.
- Clinical resource utilization.
- Hospital reputation and rankings.
- Costs associated with accreditation and regulatory audits.
- Workers' compensation claims, presenteeism, and absenteeism.
- Staff satisfaction, engagement, and burnout.
- Turnover and attraction of clinicians and staff.
- Missed referrals or decreased patient volumes.
- Hospital/research funding.
- Patient satisfaction.

2. Quantify the value drivers

Generate some initial estimates of the numerical values of those costs and benefits. You may have to shuttle between departments to do so. If you can't find specific pieces of information, make some conservative assumptions based on your knowledge, public databases, and the published literature. Be sure to note the reasons why you've made those assumptions and potential biases inherent in the data. Where you do not know the exact number, use a range. For example:

A. Value Driver	B. Current State
Turnover, expressed as human resources budget savings from recruiting and training new nurses multiplied by the average nurses who leave because of patient handling injuries per year.	Cost of recruitment and training per HR estimates and the literature: = $40k<$80k, say $60,000 Average yearly number of nurses who left because of patient handling injuries (3 years of data). Year 1: 160 nurses Year 2: 221 nurses Year 3: 243 nurses = Average 208 nurses per year Annual average turnover from patient handling injuries: = $60k * 208 = $12.5M

Story

A hospital wanted to address nursing patient handling injuries. Some of the value drivers the team identified included workers' compensation claims, absenteeism, costs from additional length of stay, reduction in lost and restricted days, turnover of staff, and patient satisfaction. Some of these drivers were already being tracked, and some were unknown.

To determine the costs of retention and recruitment, the team asked the human resources department, but found that turnover costs were not something they tracked. The team therefore used a combination of hospital information and insights from the literature to estimate the minimum, maximum, and expected costs to recruit and train new nurses, and to ascertain how many nurses had left the organization due to those injuries. Putting these together, the team was able to assess the average costs of turnover from patient handling injuries per year.

3. Forecast your impact

Now that you have calculated the current state of human and financial drivers within the system, you are in a position to generate forecasts as to the impact your project is likely to have. We do this using an approach drawn from the field of decision analysis. Be conservative here, and you must be prepared to support your arguments either from past experience, published sources, or other assessments. You probably don't know exactly what solution your team will seek to implement at this point, but you should be able to make some reasonable predictions.

Let's illustrate the remaining steps with an assessment for mitigating the costs of surgical site infections (SSIs):

a. **Identify the most significant drivers of value.**

   For example, imagine that your hospital has had an average of five SSIs per month over the last year. You know that among other factors, infections increase the cost of care and length of stay.

b. **Quantify the value driver.**

   Using a combination of hospital data and insights from the literature, you estimate the costs of each surgical site infection to be $40k, representing cost of $200k per month or $2.4M per year.

c. **Forecast impact using the 10/90/50-50 rule.**

   The 10/90/50-50 rule is a standard approach for approximating current or future values where there is a range of possible outcomes. For example, we might think that future costs of a project are $45,000 per year, but they might range from a very worst case of $100,000 to a very best case of $20,000 for different reasons.

   Using a percentage, estimate the worst, best, and most likely impact your project might have on the chosen value driver and explain the reasoning behind your assumptions.

We do it in that order so we anchor our assumptions appropriately. Look to historical data, the literature, or expert perspectives for inspiration.

- Start with the worst case. For the worst case, think of a number (x%) that would really surprise you, such that there's only a 1 in 10 chance the impact could be lower.
- For the best case, think of a number (x%) that really surprises you, such that there's only a 1 in 10 chance the impact could be higher.
- By "most likely," we are looking for a number (x%) for which there's a 50/50 chance the actual impact could be higher or lower.

For example, if you are concerned that recent personnel changes or competing priorities could hamper improvement efforts, you might draw a worst case scenario in which you will only reduce the rate to 4 per month, representing a 20% improvement. This would mean that you think there's only a 1 in 10 chance of the actual impact of your efforts being lower.

If—based on the success stories you have seen in the literature and the strength of your team—you'd be really surprised if you could reduce the total rate to only one per month, this would be your best case, representing an 80% improvement. This would mean you think there's only a 1 in 10 chance of a better outcome.

Finally, if you are confident that with some effort, there is a 50/50 chance you can reduce the infection rate from 5 down to 2 per month, this would be your most likely scenario, representing a 60% improvement.

d. Calculate the financial value of your forecasts under each scenario.

Current State

#SSIs/month	Cost per SSI	Total monthly	Total yearly
5	$40k (Length of stay and costs of care only)	$200k	$2.4M

Future State

Scenario	Estimate of Impact	#SSIs/month	Yearly Savings
Worst (only 1 in 10 chance the outcome could be lower)	Reduction from 5 infections to four per month 20%	4	$480k
Best case (only 1 in 10 chance the outcome could be higher)	Reduction from 5 infections to 1 per month 80%	1	$1.92M
Most likely (50/50 chance the outcome could be higher or lower)	Reduction from 5 infections to 2 per month 60%	2	$1.44M

e. Calculate the Expected Value.

The expected value is a calculation that takes into account your 10/90/50-50 assessments and the implications of those assessments on the associated value driver—in this case, savings from SSIs. The expected value produces a number that represents the probability-weighted mean value of your 10/90/50-50 assessments. It is not simply an average—it takes into account that you are more likely to end up in the "most likely" scenario than the other two.

So how do we move from 10/90/50-50 assessments to the expected value? This explanation may seem technical, but the calculation below, as we'll see, is simple.

The technical explanation

First, we express our 10/90/50-50 forecasts on a cumulative probability function (CPF), where they represent the 10th, 90th, and 50th percentile values.

Second, we divide the CPF into three regions where there is a 25% chance of ending up in the lowest region, a 50% chance of ending up in the middle, and a 25% chance of ending up in the highest region.

Here, the number we used to express the worst case (at the 10th percentile) is the mean of the lower region. This means we have a 25% chance of ending up in that region. The number we used to express the best case (at the 90th percentile) is the mean of the higher 25% region, and the number we used to express the most likely (at the 50th percentile) is the mean of the middle part of the distribution.

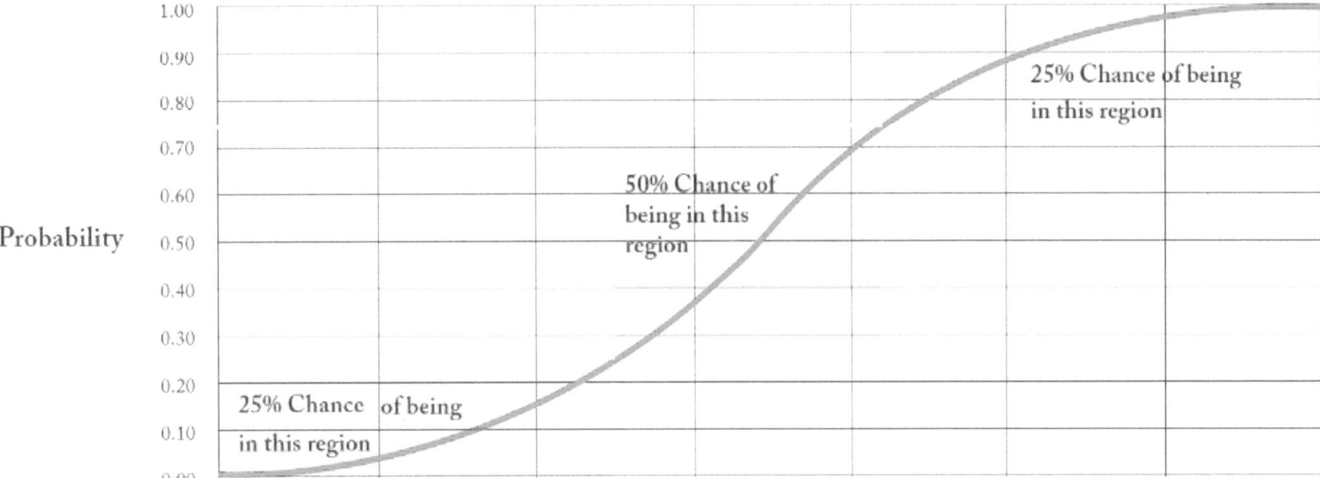

From here, we are able to determine the expected value by multiplying each of our 10/90/50-50 forecasts by the chances that we will end up in one of the three regions on the CPF.

The simple calculation

Now the simple part: The expected value is calculated by multiplying the outcome in each of our 10/90/50-50 scenarios by the associated likelihood of ending up in their region on the CPF, as follows:

Expected Value of benefits from savings in annual SSIs:

= ($1.92M x 25%) + ($1.44M x 50%) + ($480k x 25%)

= $1.32M

When we complete and include the same calculations for costs, we can assess the expected value of the project. Let's assume we've calculated that the expected costs of the project including team time, resource needs, and other costs are $500k. We are then ready to calculate the expected value of the project:

Project Expected Value = Expected benefits - Expected costs

= $1.32M - $500k

= $820k

This number represents the weighted-mean return from your project on a one-year time horizon, taking into account costs, benefits, risks, and uncertainties.

Here, we've used a limited number of value drivers. In most projects, we typically follow the same process for all of the drivers of benefit and cost we perceive to be material, usually between three and six drivers of cost, and three and six drivers of benefit.

Tip

Patient satisfaction is often difficult to quantify in financial terms. To assess the potential value of improvements to patient satisfaction, one approach is to look at the inputs and results of other hospital projects that have focused on improving patient satisfaction. Assessing the funds invested and the associated impact achieved in those projects can create a proxy for calculating the ranges of value that may be created from improvements to patient satisfaction in your project.

f. **Calculate the return on investment.**

Finally, we can determine the return on investment by dividing the project's expected value by its expected costs, expressed as a percentage—i.e., $820k/$500k = 164%—from which you may safely conclude: "Given all the possible benefits and costs, we estimate that for every $1 spent on this project, we'll save $1.64."

In this section, we've outlined a process you can use to generate initial assessments of the potential financial value of a project based on a short-term outlook. Depending on the scope of your project, this might be more than enough to establish whether efforts may be worthwhile. For some projects, value may be realized over a three to five year time horizon. In such cases we need to use a net present value calculation, which we'll introduce in Spread, the final phase of this book.

For a more comprehensive analysis that incorporates net present values, returns on investment, and internal rates of return, you should look to the finance or decision-support group within your organization, or consider using a software tool, such as The Risk Authority's Innovence Pulse solution.

The benefit of this kind of approach is that it can help teams forecast, evaluate, and then assess the financial return of their efforts by comparing actual outcomes with those forecasted. This yields significant advantages when projects have to compete against the other strategic priorities of your organization.

Step 1-4 Select your challenge

Synthesize your inputs.

You've reviewed the data, explored the system, and evaluated several problems or opportunities to pursue. The time has come to synthesize these inputs and home-in on a design challenge. An effective tool is to use a priority matrix to map your thinking and provide a useful visual for explaining your recommendation to decision makers.

Create a priority matrix

1. Make a list of your project alternatives. We recommend you consider at least three.

2. Score each alternative based on the potential for impact and your assessment of effort from 0 to 10 in the table below. Note justifications for your assessments.

   "Impact" refers to the return on investment in financial and non-financial returns.

   "Effort" refers to the difficulty of moving the project through to implementation, including such factors as executive support, access to data, available resources, project partners, time constraints, etc.

Alternatives	Impact	Effort	Justifications
Project 1	10	10	Requires team of full-time multidisciplinary experts. Three years minimum. Breakthrough returns in quality, reputation, and costs.
Project 2	6	3	A team of 4 with ad-hoc additional team members. Twelve-week time horizon and potential for significant improvements in quality. Modest returns in terms of costs and reputation.
Project 3	2	5	A complex problem not well understood in the literature. Not an institutional priority. Limited scope for impact.

Alternatives	Impact	Effort	Justifications
Project 4	8	4	A team of four over a six-month time horizon. Strong partners. Potential for significant, quantifiable reductions in liability claims and improvements to key quality indicators. Potential applications at our adult and children's hospitals. Costs may be significant.
Project 5	8	2	A team of two over twelve weeks. Potential for significant reduction in errors and high-profile stories of success.

3. Finally, plot each alternative on the priority matrix below. Potential impact goes on y-axis, and effort on the x-axis.

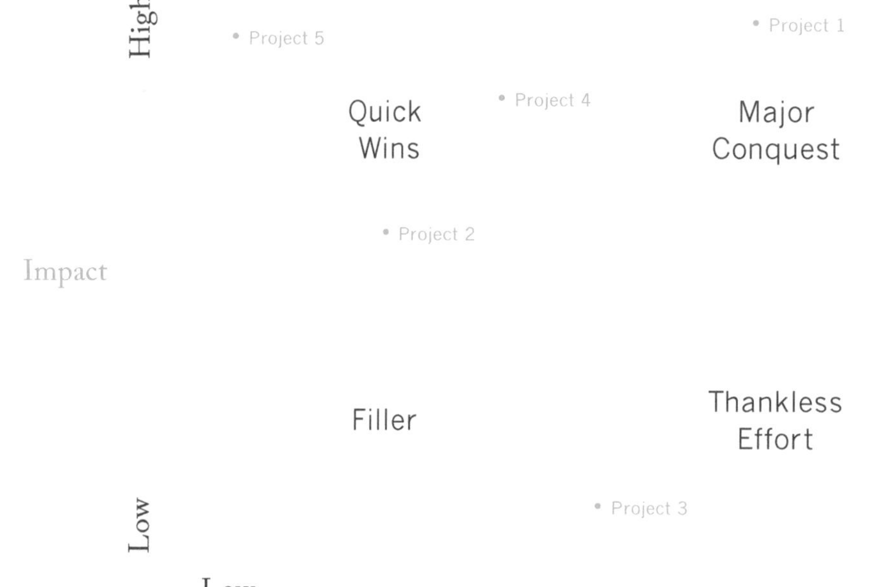

4. Select the project to which you will commit your efforts. Here's some guidance based on the matrix above:

   Quick win (High impact, low effort)

   Direct and drive your focus toward these projects. They are more likely to succeed and are more likely to provide significant returns.

   Major conquest (High impact, high effort)

   These projects are significant initiatives that require significant investments of time, resources, and capital. They can become all-consuming and leave little room for other projects. Buyer beware.

   Filler (Low impact, low effort)

   While relatively easy, these projects do not amount to much. Some of these problems can be addressed as part of day-to-day standard work; others are probably not worth your time.

   Thankless effort (Low impact, high effort)

   Beware the hard slog that yields little. These projects will bog you down, waste people's time, and offer little reward to anyone.

In the priority matrix on the opposite page, Project 5 is the clear winner. It holds the greatest promise to deliver significant returns with modest effort. The focus of your project may be determined by a host of factors beyond your control, but when backed up by solid justifications, a priority matrix can go a long way toward influencing decisions regarding how efforts should be directed.

Step 1-5 Refine the Scope

Set your parameters.

Once you have a conception of the problem space you want to work in, it's time to refine your focus. What kind of project is this? How big is it? What's in, and what's out? A properly defined project scope is critical.

What kind of project is this?

The people on your team need to know whether they should be packing flipflops or hiking boots; will they be removing a splinter or performing open-heart surgery?

Key decision makers have to be on board and aligned with the core project team as to the endpoint: what are they expecting you to deliver, and by when? These goals can be adjusted along the way as discoveries are made, as long as communication is frequent and clear.

Examples of Discovery Design projects and endpoints

Each project frame is unique, and each calls for a unique approach. There are nonetheless a handful of "types" that may serve as inspiration:

Design Project: This is a good structure for teams setting out to solve a clear, relatively discrete, known problem. Such challenges may have endpoints and clearly demarcated paths. Definitions of success can be gleaned at the start of the project: "How might we make wayfinding easier to the cath-lab?" "How might we improve [data point] for [users] by [time]?"

Discovery Project: These open-ended innovation projects provide a good structure for teams seeking inspiration and a strong call to action on a wide-challenge scope. These challenges are framed intentionally wide, have more flexibility in research modes, and have endpoints visualizing several rough, divergent, potential future states. For example: "How might we reimagine chronic care delivery inside and outside of our hospital?" "How might we reduce hospital-wide malpractice suits by 95%?" "How might we eliminate emergency department wait times?" "How might we leverage 'augmented reality' in high-risk populations?"

Alignment Project: This is a good structure for teams that feel spread thin with too many issues to address at once, yet need to move forward together. These design challenges acknowledge current issues but are framed to identify the big picture and focus on the most pressing, with a clear course of action to take next: "We have too much red tape in the ED, and we keep coming up with work-arounds. How might we re-frame our approach to emergency care?"

V2.0 Project: For teams who are at the top of their game, but with competitors on their heels. Endpoints are not incremental and push systems to think beyond current stakeholders and existing solution sets toward potential future development trajectories: "We have the highest-rated labor and delivery department in the area, but _____ down the street is also looking good. What might we look like in 3-10 years?"

"Into the Wild" Project: For teams that have completed the first steps of an idea and want to take it to the next level. Endpoints are a set of design principles, iterations or re-framings of the early ideas: "How might we launch a wearable medical device?"

Bear in mind that constraints are part of any meaningful design effort, so embrace them. Your ability to balance time, resources, and scope throughout the life of the project is essential to your success. To the extent that these anchors are fixed, your flexibility will be reduced, but you'll have clear bounds within which to work. Knowing that you can add more resources, more time, more money, more people, or lower the fidelity of the outcomes can give you greater freedom. Try to establish clear constraints to enable your team to produce timely, tangible deliverables.

Be ambitious, but scope narrowly

You might have freedom to explore new directions or you might have a mandate to improve a particular aspect of care. You still need to work out how much you are going to take on. If you begin too broadly you will find it difficult to know where to start. Conversely, a challenge that is too narrow is unlikely to inspire creative solutions.

Discovery Design works best when you can start with a specific target population and grow understanding out from there. Often times, it will be much better to take on a problem perceived to be small, score some quick wins, and as you collect momentum, take on more ambitious challenges. By contrast, tackling a topic that is too large, affects too many departments, or involves too many disciplines will often fail to produce tangible solutions within the time, resources, and attention you have to invest in it.

Be cautious also of the "platform trap," the search for a big solution that can be generalized across every situation. If this is the first project that your team is addressing with Discovery Design, it may create unrealistic expectations while you are early in the learning curve. By the same token, deliberately designing a platform robs you of the power of designing a solution that works for *these* people doing *this* specific thing. If your results are good, it is very likely that you'll be able to generalize platform principles from them and move toward a scaled solution.

For instance, improving all patient comprehension at discharge is clearly a laudable aim. However, a project focused more narrowly upon improving maternity patient comprehension at discharge will go further, and the specificity of the challenge will help you navigate system complexity, empathize meaningfully, and test implementation at a small scale.

Moreover, it is more likely that the learnings that arise from a focused exercise of this sort will apply broadly to other patients than the other way around. Don't let the impulse to generalize expand the project to an unmanageable scope.

Welcome accountability

The value of empathic and creative approaches to improving patient care is being recognized across the globe. You may have the opportunity to frame your Discovery Design projects as a way of bringing a new capability to your team. If this is your first project, encourage your sponsors to recognize that you will deliver value, not just in terms of ideas and new processes, but at the level of organizational learning, developing new skills and processes, and building understanding between groups.

If your project is well scoped and has sufficient resources, you can be confident of some degree of success by these metrics. Ensure that the senior sponsors of your initiative understand the multiple goals of the process and that this is a part of a larger journey.

Create your own accountability

Finally, and especially in organizations where chains of accountability may be obscure, it is important to establish your own accountability, as follows:

1. Define multiple success criteria that highlight dimensions of success in terms of process and outcomes. For example:
    - We will interview four surgeons, three anesthesiologists, two patients, and two caregivers.
    - We will create three prototype concepts for a new process for patient consent.
    - We will hold two feedback sessions with patients and their families.
    - We will generate a systemic approach to improving teamwork and communication in the operating room.
2. Be explicit about the time required for each step of the process.
3. Continuously measure and communicate your progress towards these goals.

This approach can influence the definition of your own success in your organization. It also creates accountability for others. For example, if you were promised access to operating room personnel and you are not receiving that access, bring that to the attention of your stakeholders at the earliest opportunity. They will understand the implications for your project and will be much more likely to provide the assistance you need.

Step 1-6 Validate your decisions

Assure decision quality.

When preparing to embark on a new project, you must ensure you're heading in the right direction. Decision analysis is a social and technical discipline widely applied in biotech, big pharma, oil and gas, and aviation—wherever an organization has to make big decisions about where to deploy its energies. Many of its tools, such as the decision quality chain, have proven useful in helping a team determine whether it is ready to go forward. The chain works by defining the six elements that go into making a good decision, with the assumption that a decision is only as good as its weakest link. Here, we've adapted it to the specific question of whether you're ready to move from Scope to Prepare.

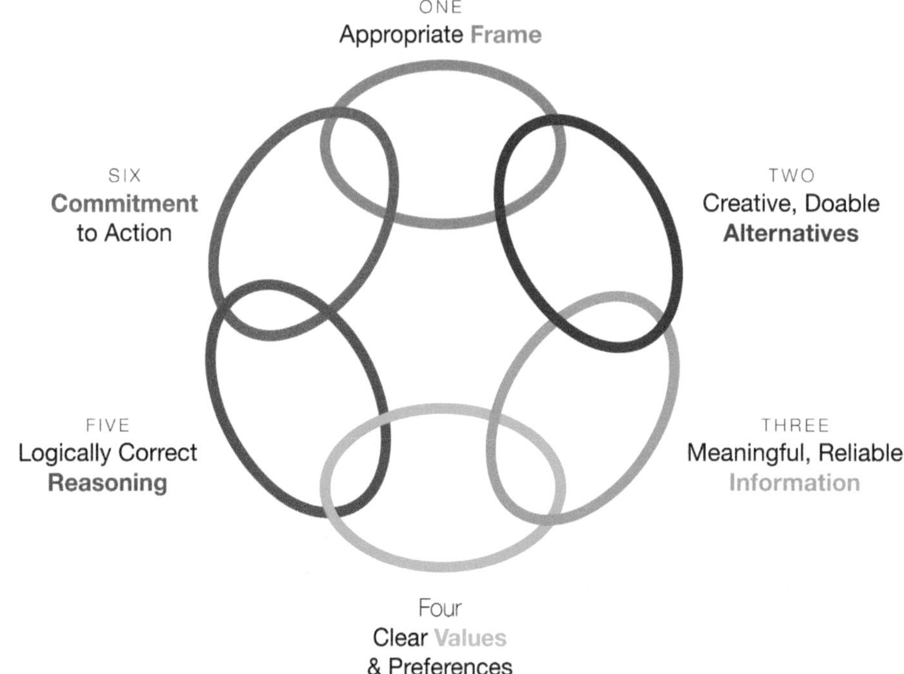

First, let's look at the six elements of the decision quality chain, and then use a radar plot to check whether we've done enough to assure we're making a good decision to go forward with the chosen project:

Appropriate Frame

What are we deciding?
When do we need to make the decision?
Who needs to be involved?

A clear, well-defined frame will help focus the team on the real task at hand.

- Are we clear on what we are deciding? For example, are our decision makers on board with the project's scope?
- Who do we need to involve? Have we consulted the necessary stakeholders?
- What's on the table? What is off the table? For example, have we been asked to improve medication reconciliation quality upon admission, or explore opportunities to redesign the process across the continuum of care?
- When do we need to do this? Are we expected to deliver before the next board meeting? What can we decide later?

Creative, Doable Alternatives What choices do we have?	We always compare multiple areas of concern before selecting the one on which we will focus our energies. This helps ensure we pursue the ripest opportunity. • Have we evaluated at least three to five potential problem areas? • Have we surveyed leaders, potential partners, and key stakeholders to see what kind of topics they would be interested in working on?
Meaningful, Reliable Information What do we know?	Basing your project frame and scope on solid footing will help refine your focus. • Are you clear-minded as to what the data is saying? • Are you using relevant and trustworthy facts about the past? • Are you using unbiased judgments about the present or future? • Have you explored the system and reviewed the literature to understand what is already being done in this area? • Have you considered and communicated project unknowns?
Clear Values & Preferences What consequences do we care about? What do we want and don't want to happen?	There are some problems the organization may not be "ready" for. Here, we need to make tradeoffs. • Is the project congruent with executive priorities? • Does the problem resonate with the relevant stakeholders? • Does the topic impact on the presumption of "zero harm?" • Are you confident this project can result in a "win?"
Logically Correct Reasoning Are we thinking straight?	Hasty decisions are risky decisions, and many factors can bias your focus away from problem spaces that are more optimal, important, or appropriate to work on. • Have you followed a logical, formal process for making this decision? • Are you confident you are starting off on solid footing? You should be able to clearly articulate, "we are choosing this project because..."
Commitment to Action Will we act? Will it get done?	Ideas are only as good as the actions that are taken upon them. Give yourself the greatest prospects of success. • Is there a solid pipeline to implementation? • Are you clear on the endpoint? What does "good" look like? • Do you have enough runway and time to get this done? • Do you have sufficient executive and managerial commitment to support the project through to completion?

Create a radar plot

A radar plot can be used to evaluate the quality of your decision process and assess whether a team is ready to move forward with a plan. In this exercise:

1. List the decision quality elements along each spoke on the radar plot.
2. Using the criteria below, score your project against each element out of 10.
    - A score of 10 means you have very high clarity and confidence that you've met the quality indicators; you are indicating that 9 times out of 10, you've done everything you can do to assure success.
    - A score of 5 out 10 means you're very uncertain; there is a 50/50 chance it could go either way.
    - A score below 5 is indicative of known gaps and deficiencies. Remember: the quality of your decision is only as good as the weakest link!
3. Develop and execute an action plan for improving the quality of each element in your decision. Use your best efforts to push your scores for each criteria as high as possible. Your work is done when significant further efforts become infeasible in light of your resource and time constraints.

How might you use this approach for determining where to direct your efforts? One of our client's project teams was commissioned to start a project focused on the hospital's most significant driver of clinical risks. The data revealed that surgical errors were the primary driver, with cardiac diagnostic errors and adverse drug events in second and third place.

However, after exploring the system, the team learned of significant departmental leadership changes, shifting priorities, and that several other projects had stalled. The team noted serious concerns as to whether the project would have sufficient commitment to action and therefore scored that project as 5/10.

The team also explored a project focused on cardiac diagnostic errors. After the Institute of Medicine's report on diagnostic errors in 2017, there was major interest from key stakeholders to take on a major project. The nature and source of "diagnostic" errors was hard to frame, but the team considered that that would be a major focus of the project. They therefore scored the project for that element as 8/10.

Using the radar plots shown below, the team compared the project alternatives based on the decision quality criteria. Given that a decision is only as good as its weakest link, the Surgical Errors Project scored a barely passable 5/10, where as the Cardiac Diagnostic Errors Project scored 7/10.

The team shared their decision process with their stakeholders, and received the go-ahead to start a six-month project on reducing cardiac diagnostic errors.

Surgical Errors Project

ONE
Appropriate Frame

TWO
Creative, Doable Alternatives

THREE
Meaningful, Reliable Information

Four
Clear Values & Preferences

FIVE
Logically Correct Reasoning

SIX
Commitment to Action

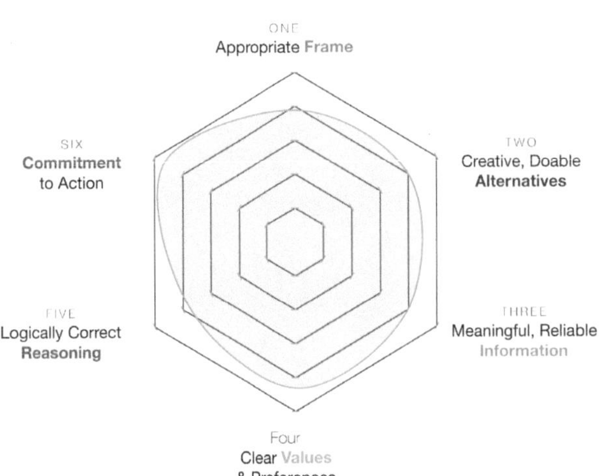

The selective use of tools such as these will help avoid unforeseen pitfalls by bringing to the fore areas that may require further research.

Step 1-7 Secure a mandate

Get the necessary buy-in.

Once you are confident that you have identified a problem space that is supported by the data, is institutionally appropriate, holds promise to deliver a sufficient return on investment, and is proportionate to the time, resources, and outputs you will need to deliver, it's time to create and present a concise project proposal to your stakeholders.

All parties must be fully aligned on the scope of the project and what the expected outputs will be. This will be critical in releasing the appropriate resources to your team and garnering the sufficient buy-in across the organization.

Whether the proposal takes the form of a one-page report, a chart, or a PowerPoint deck, confining the summary to one page helps to focus your thinking and provides a useful executive summary for sharing with senior stakeholders.

Project Name

Create a unique name for your project that captures interest. Your project name should inspire people.

Project Sponsor/s

Who is/are the senior leader/s with ultimate oversight for the project?

Project Lead/s

List the key contacts for the project.

Objective

Generate a concise statement of what the project is intended to achieve. At this stage, this can be narrow, bold, or aspirational.

Background

Include important background or context for the project. Why is this important at your organization? How important is this nationally and beyond? What's been done?

Problem Overview

What is the problem (expressed in data, financials, or otherwise)?
Where is it occurring? Who are the key stakeholders and end users?
What are our current hypotheses as to why the problem exists?
What are the unknowns about the problem?
What are the costs or risks of doing nothing?

Milestones & Deliverables

Description of the desired impact and timing of the key milestones and outputs of your project. Use the Discovery Design phases as a guide. What constitutes success? What is the reporting mechanism? For example:

Approach

Short summary of the proposed approach and activities to solve the problem.

Constraints

Items that are out of scope or other guardrails of the project.

Team

Who is responsible for the work? Who are you partnering with?

Budget & Resources

Time, material, finance, and human resource requests.

You have now scoped the project. It's time to build your team, create a plan, and assemble the resources that will enable you to tackle it.

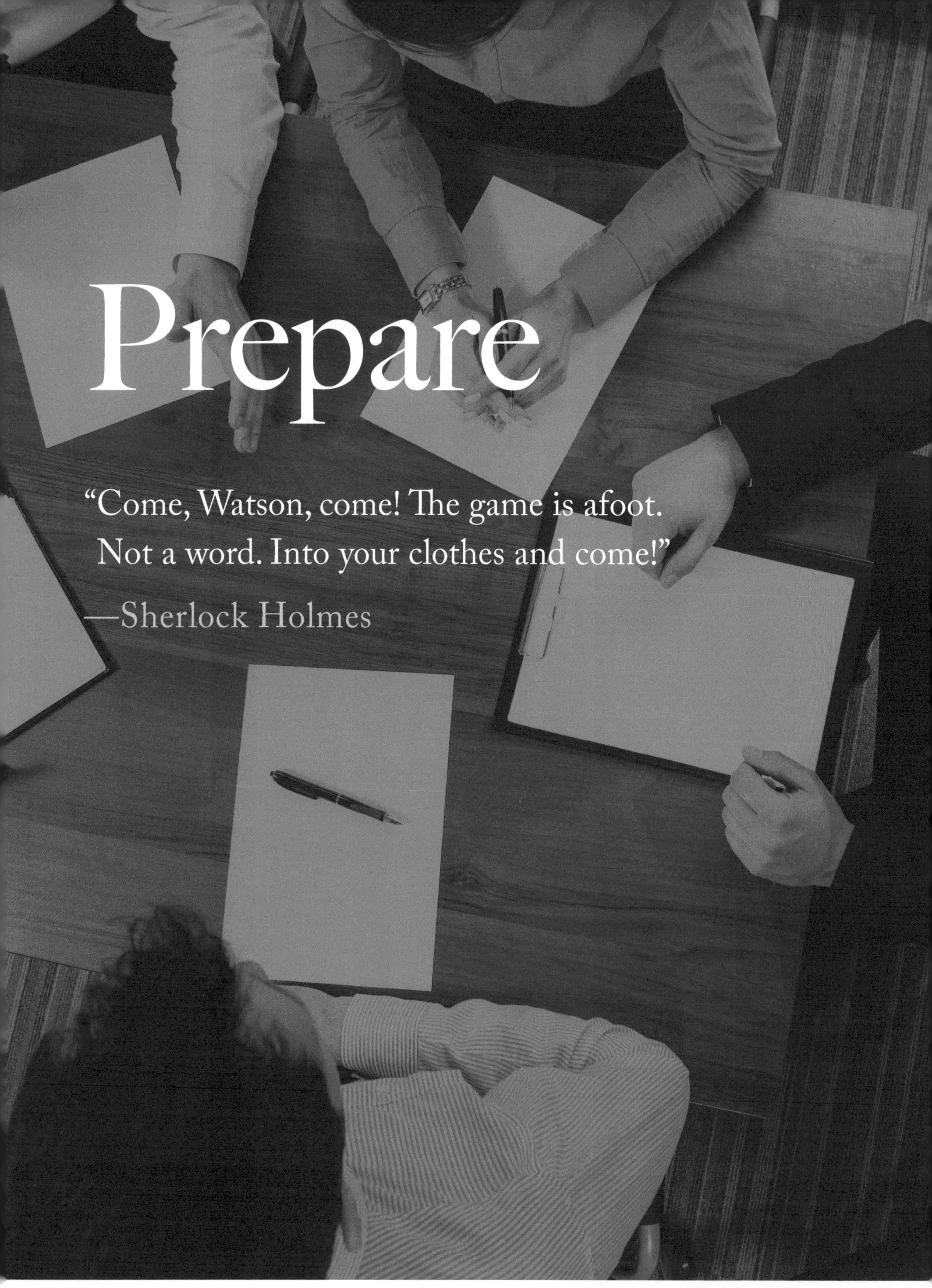

Prepare

"Come, Watson, come! The game is afoot. Not a word. Into your clothes and come!"

—Sherlock Holmes

Starting a new project is like moving a boulder. It takes an enormous amount of effort at the start, but once it gets rolling, momentum takes over and the process itself gives you energy and direction. In Phase 2 of the Discovery Design process—Prepare—you will begin gathering the elements you'll need to get started: a team, a plan, a space, and materials. By the end, you will be ready to begin your exploration of the problem space, seeking to identify opportunities for design.

Process steps

Step 2-1 Build your team

Build project and advisor teams to support rapid decision making.

Step 2-2 Create a project plan

Determine where you should be, who will do what, and what you will need.

Step 2-3 Prepare space and materials

Create a dedicated innovation space for your work to flourish.

Step 2-4 Dot the i's and cross the t's

Address privacy, regulatory, insurance, ethical, resource, and other considerations.

Step 2-5 Host a team kickoff

Rally your team, discuss the calendar, and share what you know.

Step 2–1 Build your team

Build project and advisor teams to support rapid decision making.

In the field of healthcare improvement, we are often asking people to abandon the status quo and embrace the unknown. Decision makers who are tasked with ensuring stability are naturally risk-averse and may be wary of initiatives where outcomes may be uncertain. It's of the utmost importance, then, to engage in an ongoing, collaborative dialogue with the stakeholders and community surrounding your project.

Any design effort should seek to make everyone's life better and no one's worse. This is especially important in healthcare, where a single change can affect a broad spectrum of people ranging from physicians, pharmacists, and nurses to patients, their families, and community stakeholders. Inevitably, organizational politics will affect whether an idea is accepted and implemented, but you can mitigate their effect by building a community of support and maintaining it through the life of the project.

The first step in preparing to launch your project, then, is to identify the key stakeholders and begin building a network. This will include a core team that will be tasked with moving the project forward and is responsible for producing results; sponsors who provide high-level support, oversight, and accountability; partners who will take responsibility for various aspects of the work; adopters who are the first to try, develop, and test new solutions; and finally, scalers, whose role is to spread the idea throughout the organization. In some organizations, these groups will be completely disparate; in others, they will overlap.

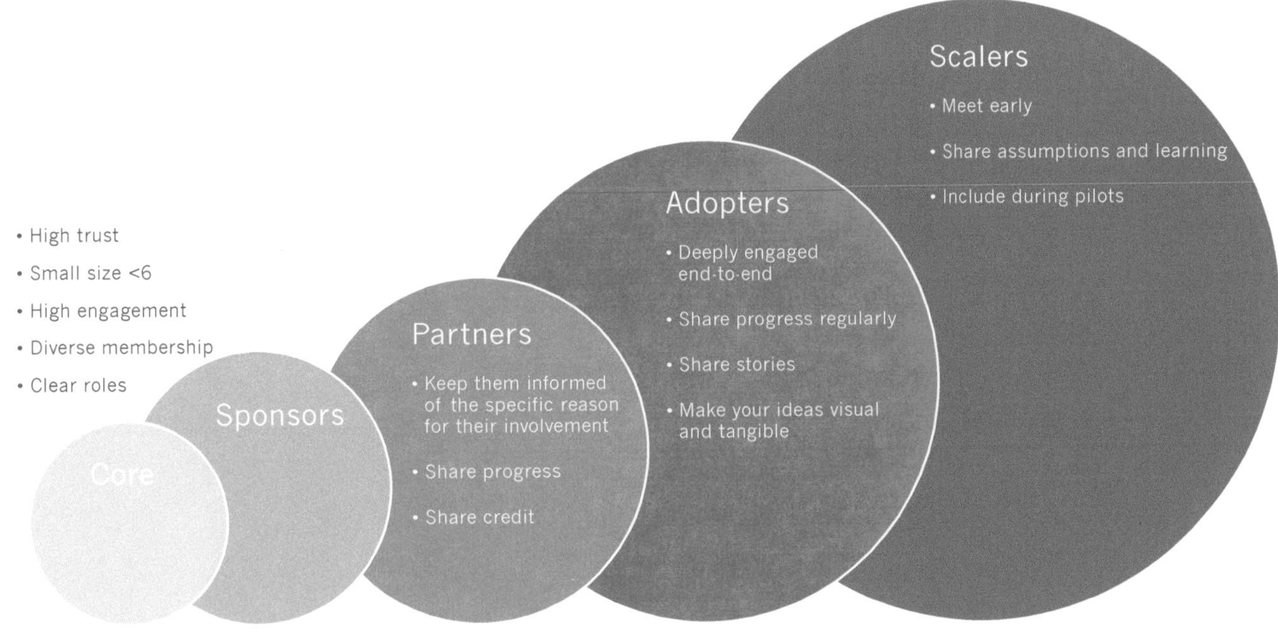

The Core Team

Design is a team sport. As you go about the important work of building your core team, we suggest some factors that will influence its success:

High trust

The most important indicators of team performance are less about who is on the team and more about how the team works together. High-trusting teams are high performing teams and the ability to build trust is dependent on the values and personalities of team members, and the culture you are able to create together. The strongest teams:

- offer vulnerability: people are willing to take risks and be vulnerable in front of other team members; people who are comfortable with bringing their "whole selves" to their work.
- demonstrate empathy: people care about their colleagues as people, pay attention to the unspoken needs and mental states of others, and are able to respond effectively and empathically.
- are flexible: people are comfortable with ambiguity and operate effectively when the path forward becomes unclear.
- stoke optimism: people bring optimism and energy to the team, and add value and encouragement by their example.
- model dependability: people deliver on their commitments on time and with excellence.
- are mission-driven: people see their work as a purposeful and connected with meaning; they really care about making a difference.
- are supportive: people support each other through confidentiality, dialogue, mediation, and encouragement when the going gets tough; they would never "throw someone under the bus."
- build friendship: people are inclusive in interpersonal settings and look for opportunities to get to know each other; you might see them take each other to coffee, lunch, happy hour, or outings.

Story:

In 2012, a team from Google launched a project code-named "Aristotle" to identify the elements that made some teams succeed and others flounder. They surveyed 180 of their teams across the globe, and discovered that the number one determinant of performance was "psychological safety," defined by the study lead as "a blend of trust, respect for each other's competence, and caring about each other as people." Teams with high psychological safety exceeded their targets by, on average, 17%. In contrast, those with low psychological safety missed their targets by, on average, 19%. In these teams, members feel safe to take risks and be vulnerable with others without feeling insecure or embarrassed.

Small size

The optimal size for an effective core team is three to five people. Two is a bare minimum, and more than six can slow you down. Creative ideas emerge from the team, and there are also practical tasks that require collaboration. For example, during interviews, it is useful for one person to talk and the other to listen and take notes; a single person cannot do the job alone.

Larger groups tend to diffuse responsibility and increase the burden of team management. More importantly, it becomes impossible for the group to meet productively and form a cohesive, collective view of the project. During later phases, teams can grow much larger, and complex tasks involving execution and implementation can be subdivided into smaller ones.

High engagement

It's often the case that teams will need to juggle multiple projects as well as their routine jobs. Nevertheless, effective projects demand high focus and high engagement from every member of the core team. Your core team should commit to meeting at least weekly and communicating daily.

Watch out for "partial commitments." Team members who are neither in nor out are more likely to be disruptive than to make a positive contribution. The team will be distracted by the need to bring the partial member up to speed.

Diverse membership

A mix of thinkers, doers, and makers will greatly enhance the group's ability to deal with the complex challenges facing any healthcare organization. Aim for people who bring different backgrounds, skills, strengths, and perspectives, and who love collaboration.

Consider including someone from your Risk, Safety, and Quality office; a nurse or a physician. Try including a patient (most organizations have a patient advocate or patient council) or someone from Social Work or Guest Services. Don't forget people who can speak to the needs of management in addition to those who understand the shop floor.

Beyond their formal roles, think about individuals who might bring a unique skill to the team, such as facilitation, storytelling, system thinking, etc. The best teams include visionaries who are able to see the way ahead and task-oriented "doers" with a reputation for getting things done.

Here are two examples from some recent projects:

- The core team on a design project focused on improving patient experience after adverse surgical outcomes consisted of a VP-level sponsor (time commitment 5%), two senior risk managers (20%), one patient advocate (20%), a project administrator (40%), and one designer (20%).
- An open-innovation project on medication administration safety included a VP-level sponsor (time commitment 10%), a project lead (50%), two designers (80% and 40%), a pediatric cardiology nurse (25%), a senior RN in Quality and Safety (20%), and a Human Factors fellow (25%).

Clear roles

It helps if all members of the team feel they've been assigned to roles in which they can add maximum value, such as:

- the leader who has overall responsibility for the project
- the communicator who keeps all the key stakeholders up to date
- the energizer who pushes the big ideas and fuels the enthusiasm
- the coordinator who keeps everyone on track
- the ambassador who is skilled at negotiation and conflict resolution

Sponsors

In most organizations, it will be necessary to have a sponsor who will support your goals, authorize your budget, and provide advice and resources. Depending on the scope of your project, your sponsor should:

- be involved in key decision points
- check in periodically, at least every two months
- join periodic report-outs
- provide advice, consent, and endorsement

> "Not finance. Not strategy. Not technology. It is teamwork that remains the ultimate competitive advantage, both because it is so powerful and so rare."
>
> —Patrick Lencioni

Your sponsors will typically be one to three key stakeholders and decision makers who have the authority to deploy resources and set priorities. This may include members of the executive team, key mid-level managers, or anyone who has the power to remove barriers and roadblocks for your project.

We recommend that you have one executive who has decision-making authority over the project and others as necessary for buy-in, advice, consent, and support. But beware of too many cooks!

If you don't have an official sponsor, identify a friendly ally in leadership who should be kept informed about your work. Senior stakeholders should be aware of your project at key stages throughout the process, especially at moments such as:

- decisions around the framing and launch of the project
- learning from Discovery and Synthesize
- the review of proposed design solutions
- the decision to implement
- the review of the implementation and pilot plan
- monitoring, evaluating, and celebrating impact

Partners

Partners can include people from across the health system who should be kept up to date as the project unfolds, but who may not need to be part of the core team or the sponsor team. There may also be people who have key skills that can be useful during one section of the project. The more people know about your project from the beginning, the more resources you will have to help with knowledge expertise, recruiting, bridge building, and gate keeping. Their support can be extraordinarily helpful to the success of the project.

Partners may come from affiliated parts of your organization that share points of common interest. They should expect you to:

- keep them informed of the specific reason for their involvement
- share progress
- share credit

Adopters

The people who will actually implement your design solution should be part of your extended team. With adopters you should:

- share progress regularly
- tell stories
- make your ideas visual and tangible

It is imperative that you involve those who will eventually adopt your solution and keep them informed about what you are doing along the way. Ensure that you share progress with the adopter group via periodic report-outs. Share stories and photos with them, and work out ways to make progress on the project seem visible and tangible. Host milestone workshops throughout the project to demonstrate that you have incorporated their feedback and involved them in the ultimate design of the solution.

Scalers

If you are to implement your ideas across your entire organization, you will need help on many fronts. To prepare those who will help you scale your ideas, you must:

- meet early
- share your assumptions and learning
- gather their feedback during pilots

Your ultimate goal is to disseminate your solution throughout the organization. You'll therefore need to meet early with managers and leaders of groups who will eventually adopt your idea once it has been proven in a test environment. Meet with them one-on-one, collect their feedback, and think of them as part of your extended project team. Share your assumptions and learning with them, and invite them to participate during pilots.

> "You can design and create, and build the most wonderful place in the world. But it takes people to make the dream a reality."
>
> —Walt Disney

Build your team

The goal of this exercise is to build an inclusive project team, identify sponsors and partners, recruit key decision makers and gatekeepers, and mobilize the groups that will eventually adopt your solution and those that will scale it.

1. Using sticky notes, brainstorm all of the people who relate to the problem space of your project. You can be as general as a whole group ("residents") or as specific as a particular person ("Nurse Jones").
2. Cluster the stakeholders into the following groups:
    - Core team
    - Sponsors
    - Partners
    - Adopters
    - Scalers
3. For each key group, come up with a statement that expresses their key concern, motivation, or expectations.
4. Assign priorities to each stakeholder group or person based on the importance of their engagement in the project and the value that they might bring. Remove those who are of less importance to the project.
5. Finally, list the names of key individuals in each group and assign a role for each of them. For example, a chief medical officer may be a key project sponsor. That person's role in the project might be to provide advice at key decision points or simple administrative cover. Then set a goal in regard to that advisor—for instance, to meet with them once a month throughout the life of the project.

Stakeholder Guide

Core Project Team

TEAM MEMBER NAME	ROLES AND GOALS

Sponsors

SPONSOR NAME	ROLES AND GOALS

Partners

PARTNER NAME	ROLES AND GOALS

Adopters

ADOPTER NAME	ROLES AND GOALS

Scalers

SCALER NAME	ROLES AND GOALS

"500 coffees"

Now: meet, meet, meet. Informal conversations are often better for finding alignment than emails or cold telephone calls. Talk to many people up and down the organization, beginning with "friendly allies" and expanding from there. As you go, look for people with the following characteristics:

- People whose own agendas will benefit from your project
- People who have a track record of "getting it done"
- People with skill sets that complement your own
- People who are spoken of highly by leaders and frontline stakeholders
- People who are excited about the problem you want to work on
- People with whom you feel you can have a vibrant working relationship
- People who are fun to work with!

This was our core team on a recent clinical risk management project: a clinical nurse specialist, a lawyer, an anthropologist, and a communications designer. Everyone brought something completely different to the team and trust and momentum was built by setting an intention to meet outside the office at regular intervals.

Step 2-2 Create a project plan

Determine what should be done, who will do what, and what they will need.

Once you have defined the scope and direction of your project and identified the people that will form your team, the next step is to create a detailed project plan. You will avoid a fuzzy front end and get your project off to a running start if you forecast the challenges you are likely to encounter along the way and the resources you'll need to meet them. Book meetings for the entire project now. A project plan will give you a sense of the tasks that await you and the logistics you will need in order to realize it.

Timeline

The sample project chart below shows a suggested timeline based on a twelve-week project, two to three FTEs with 50+% dedicated time to the project. But how you divide out your efforts between the different phases may vary significantly, depending on the scope of the challenge that you are taking on. Completing the process entirely in twelve weeks is realistic for a relatively constrained scope—one that exists within a single team or redesigning a specific discrete element of a system.

For more ambitious scopes, you may have to divide the eight steps into two or three twelve-week design cycles, each building on the other. It is important that you give yourself enough time to achieve real results, but not so much time that your team loses momentum along the way. As you review the various steps in this handbook, assess how much time you will need for each task, and be prepared to discover additional directions you'll want to explore and others that can be passed over.

Example Timeline

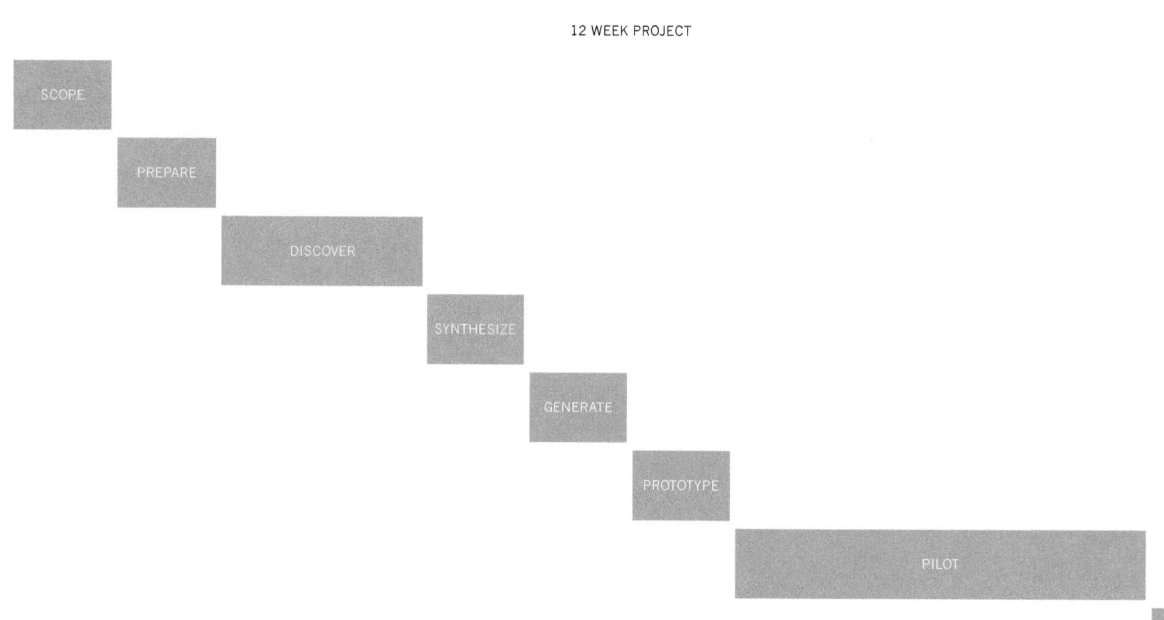

Advance planning

It's a good idea to plan your workshop and key meetings as far in advance as possible; we recommend you print out our twelve week or six month project poster and mark key meetings, activities, and dates so that all members of the team can plan accordingly (people in more traditional organizations may not be used to moving as quickly). Set major deadlines as early as possible, and try to identify the tasks that are most likely to hold you up.

The biggest challenge to your timeline is likely to be finding people to observe in context and setting up interview times; this can be difficult, so in any Discovery Design, this should be your top priority. Once you have determined the number of observations you will need and figured out how to gain access to the people you want to meet, you are ready to build a plan.

The key meetings should include the following:

- **Project kickoff**
  This gathering will serve to get everyone on the same page and build energy and momentum.
- **Synthesize review**
  Along the way it will be necessary to review research findings, consider new opportunities, and confirm directions to pursue. This is an opportunity for the wider team to hear stories from the field and to bring your research findings to life. By the end of this meeting you should have identified top user needs and developed a solid framework for addressing them.
- **Solutions review**
  Review assessed solutions and recommendations. As the project advances toward its conclusion, you will need to gather the core team, key decision makers, and perhaps invite experts to share their viewpoints.

A project tracker can be a very helpful tool to help plan everything that needs to be done, especially those activities that may be dependent on others or where bottlenecks might arise. For example, you might need the chief medical officer's support to launch the project, but there might be three other committees that oversee the workflow you intend to change. When do they next meet? How long will the review take? What are they likely to say? Space, staffing, uniforms, permissions, time, material, cash on hand, and many other details will all need to be thought through. It's not uncommon for a chart to include hundreds of tasks.

Beware of what Nobel laureate Daniel Kahneman described as the planning fallacy: the tendency for people to grossly underestimate the time that will be needed to complete a task. Leave sufficient slack in the project to account for unexpected delays. Try to assume that everything will take three times longer than you think is reasonable. And even that might not be enough.

Here is a very simple Excel tracker for a 6-month project that you can adapt to your needs. Follow along on the very top menu bar:

- Tasks: Note all of your tasks and subtasks in the Task column. In this example, we have greatly simplified the plan by noting the project phases only. You might identify anywhere from dozens to hundreds of tasks depending on the complexity of your project.
- Schedule: Enter your plan according to the hours, days, weeks, or months that your pilot will run. We recommend you track progress against a daily or weekly timeline. As you move through the project, note which week you are in using a big dotted line denoting the beginning of the next phase. In this example, we are half way through Discover & Synthesize. Shade in the box when each particular task is meant to be completed on or by. Whenever a task is complete, place a big X in the relevant schedule box or shade it in.
- People: Next, note who will be responsible for each task and those who will be helping them.

- Resources: List all the resources that will be needed to complete each task. This exercise usually uncovers additional tasks that need to be completed to gather them!
- Comments: Finally, use the Comments and Tracking box to communicate updates with your team at your daily or weekly huddles.
- Tracking: As you move throughout the pilot, indicate whether tasks are on track, falling behind, or require escalation by shading the relevant box in green, orange, or red.

Green means the task is proceeding satisfactorily: on time, as desired.
Orange means the task is at risk of delay or partial completion, but the team can fix it and is working on it.
Red means the task is at risk of failure, and the team needs to escalate the matter for attention.

Example

TASKS	Project Schedule	Team Lead & Helpers	Resources Needed	Comments and Tracking
	J F M A M J			
Scope & Prepare	x	Lucie & Simon	Analyst Project space Meeting with CMO	1/15: Proposal accepted. 1/30: Project plan built; team recruited. Ready to go.
Discover & Synthesize	x	Kara & Svava + Improvement team on CU456	Permissions, camera, supplies, workroom at the hospital	2/28: Research complete 3/1: Preparing for synthesize review
Generate & Prototype		Rob & Soren leading workshops	Funds to pay for nurses' time	2/28: We do not have funds for nurses time. Svava to meet with CNO.
Pilot & Spread		Simon & Shannon	Build measurement tools. IRB submission.	3/4: Rob has submitted IRB
Tracker	Performing Satisfactory	Requires Action	Requires Escalation	

Create a visual calendar

A physical calendar can supercharge a project and set a steady drumbeat of progress; just remember to honor it without being enslaved by it. Unlike digital calendars, which tell you where you are, an analog calendar tells you how far you have traveled and how much remains to be done.

- Print a large poster that contains the full length of the project, and hang it visibly in the project space. No access to large printers? Draw it, use sticky notes and get creative. See an example of one of ours below.
- Use sticky notes to map out your plan. Add key dates, team vacations, or any other calendar keep-outs. Be as explicit and exact as possible. Don't shy away from picking placeholder dates until meetings are confirmed, or from blocking off entire weeks for one phase of the design process.
- Review the timeline, and notice any bottlenecks or areas where you might need additional resources.

"It takes time to create excellence. If it could be done quickly, more people would do it."

—John Wooden

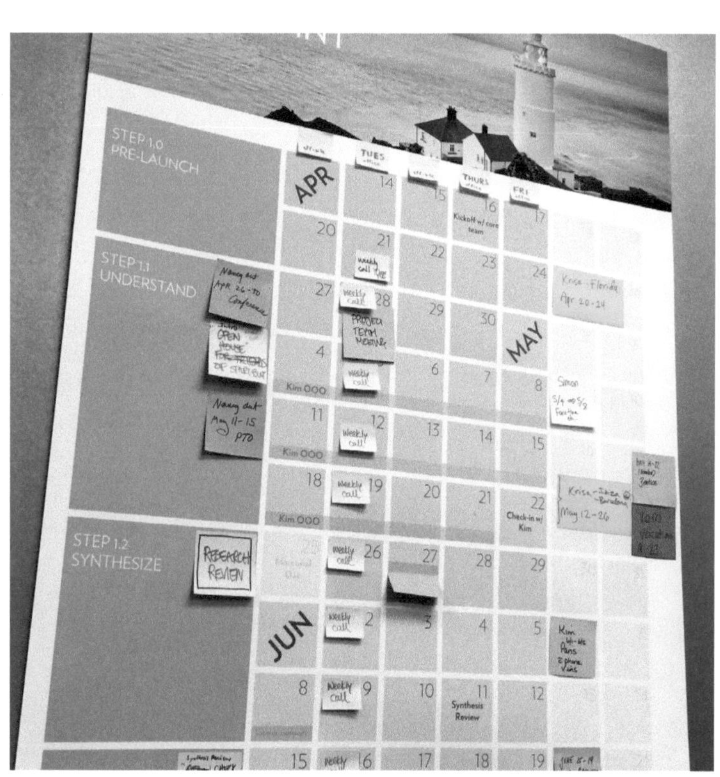

Once you have created a timetable you must do whatever is necessary to protect it! Set the pace for your team, whether it's a weekly meeting or daily huddle, and use these tools to track and monitor progress throughout the pilot. Determine where they will live: a project wall, email, Google Docs, #Slack, Basecamp, or an iMessage thread—whatever you and your team determine will work best for them!

Conduct a pre-mortem

Have you thought of everything you need to do or need to account for? Probably not. A powerful tool for uncovering the reasons your project might become delayed or derailed is to conduct a project "pre-mortem" with your team. We view this as a critical step for setting yourself up with the maximum prospects of success.

1. Gather your team. Give everyone sticky notes and a marker.
2. Ask everyone to imagine that the project has failed spectacularly and to write down every reason they can think of for the failure (one idea per sticky note).
3. Next, ask team members to read their reasons and post the sticky notes on a board. Keep going until all have been placed on the board. Cluster the sticky notes into themes, and review the list.
4. Here is the most important step: in response to each of the major risks to your project, come up with concrete, tangible strategies you will employ to avoid those problems. Then strengthen the project plan.
5. Now, inform the team that the project has succeeded beyond your wildest expectations. Ask the team to generate as many reasons as they can for why the project was so successful.
6. Repeat steps 3 to 4, this time coming up with tangible strategies you will employ to maximize your chances of success.

Introduce the Discovery Design mood map

Healthcare projects are hard, and your team (and senior stakeholders) must be prepared for an exciting but uncertain emotional journey. We have observed a characteristic cycle for every Discovery Design project, which we fine very helpful to acknowledge in advance. See the description for each stage of the diagram on the opposite page.

Preview this journey during the kick off and explain to the team that progress is not linear. They will need to trust the process, buoyed by the knowledge that they are tackling hard problems that don't necessarily have easy solutions. Advise them that there will be periods when they may feel overwhelmed and discouraged, but that this is normal and to be expected.

Give your team opportunities throughout the project to express where they feel like they're at along the mood map journey. Enabling safe space for this kind of vulnerability creates an atmosphere of trust and empathy among the team. And high trust teams are not just significantly more effective, they're more fun to be part of!

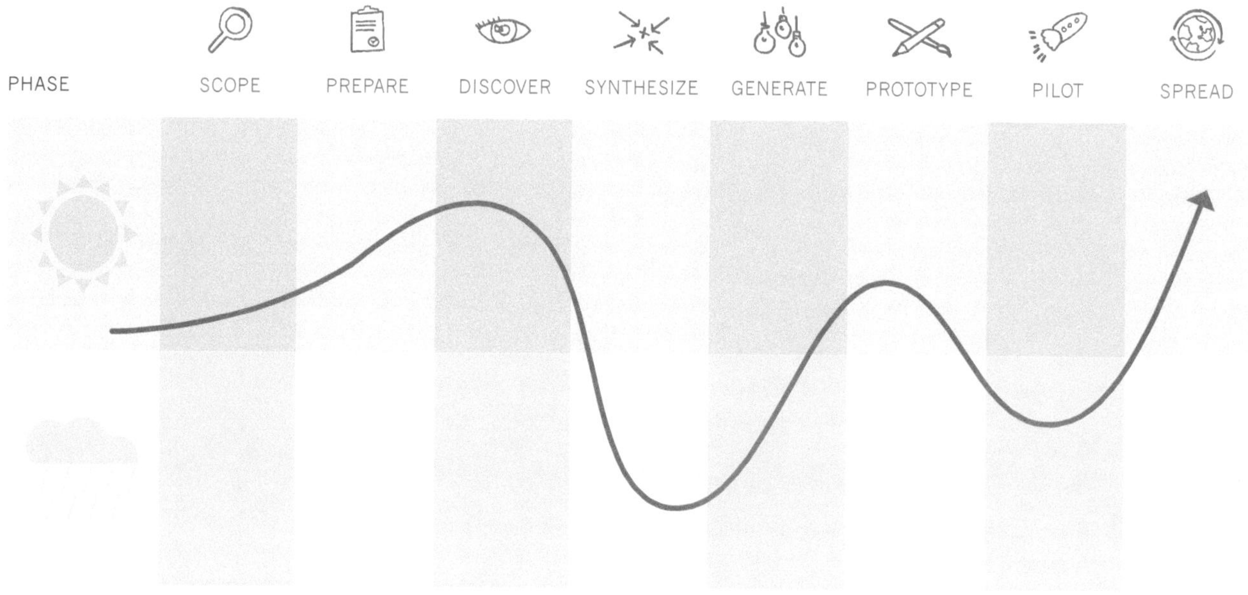

Scope & Prepare	**Excitement!** There is great optimism and enthusiasm about the new project. The sky's the limit, and the team is excited to engage with this important topic.
Discover	**Inspiration! And then, the slide.** The first observations often create an emotional high as team members are learning quickly in the real world. "Low hanging fruit" beckons, and as the team begins to understand the outline of the system, everything is coming into focus. As observations accumulate, so too does the evidence of the complexity of your challenge. Initial hypotheses seem superficial and the amount of information becomes overwhelming. Morale starts to waver. You have entered the slide.
Synthesize	**The trough. And then, the light.** As the team starts to synthesize its findings, the mood bottoms out. Wrangling all the perspectives seems impossible. Every idea has been thought of before, and useful insights and patterns are elusive. Time and resources are running thin, or perhaps a key team member has been called off the project. The team holds to the mantra, "Trust the process." And then, bright spots start to emerge: little moments of clarity are the proof that the team is making progress. A single insight lifts the team's energy, but we are not out of the woods yet. Eventually, design opportunities appear that capture the interest and engagement of end users. From synthesis, a concrete and meaningful design challenge!
Generate & Prototype	**Possibilities and new directions open!** Teams come together to brainstorm and explore new solutions. Energy and excitement brings a host of ideas to the surface. New concepts are proposed and shared. Some are rejected entirely; some provide valuable feedback for way forwards. You are at the beginning of the upward slope.
Pilot	**Rubber hits the road, reality strikes, ahas and robustness emerge.** New ideas begin to show promise in the environment. The team is grappling with how to implement a new idea in a dynamic system. New stakeholders, constraints, and complexities come to the fore. A favorite idea proves infeasible and needs to be let go. Through various pilots, however, the solution takes shape. Team moves from refinement to validation by collecting data and stories of impact.
Spread	**Enthusiasm, vision, impact.** In the final stages, the team sees the light! Bringing together everything that has been learned suddenly reveals the robustness of the thinking that has been done. People enter into storytelling mode, presenting testimonies and data that reveal impact, and honor people who've been part of the journey. Senior stakeholders give approval to implement and spread the idea across the organization. New systems, processes, and requirements are codified. What were once prototypes are now policy!

Create a communications plan

It is essential to establish a rhythm for maintaining momentum throughout the project. There's no single formula for this, and you should determine what works best for your team. You may find this framework useful:

Touch point	Description	Agenda
Daily huddles	A very short 5-minute standing meeting every morning with your core team is a great way to build teamwork, ensure high communication, and boost morale.	• What did you accomplish yesterday? • Top priorities for the day. • Share roadblocks that you need help with (team members should help after the huddle, not during!). • Recognize and celebrate wins.
Weekly project team check-in	A 30-minute video or teleconference for your project team and selected partners as appropriate to keep them informed. Print a simple one-page agenda for each meeting to memorialize the status and share with those unable to join the call.	• Project status: where are we? • Strategic priorities: primary focus/secondary focus. • Current status in detail: key milestones, progress reports, comments, next steps, and follow-up items. • Looking ahead to the following week. • Gut check: what's on your mind?

Touch point	Description	Agenda
Monthly project newsletter	An effective way to corral the core team, sponsors, partners, stakeholders, front line staff, and community members who might be interested in the project is to send out a periodic newsletter at key milestones during the project. Microsoft Word and Apple Pages have good newsletter templates you can use. We'd suggest you block out one hour after each key milestone to put your newsletter together.	This can simply be one page, including some (de-identified if appropriate) photographs that bring some of the project activities to life, a short description of what has been happening, and what is coming next. Key milestones might include the following: • Project Kickoff • Discovery Phase • Synthesize Phase • Ideation Review • Launch Review • Monitoring Phase
Stakeholder check-ins (Every 4 to 6 weeks)	An effective strategy for keeping project sponsors and other senior key stakeholders informed and involved in your project is via periodic check-ins to share progress, ask advice, and present specific requests for support.	• Progress reports • Key wins • Obstacles • Specific requests for support • What's next

Step 2-3 Space and materials

Create a dedicated innovation space for your work to flourish.

Carve out some physical space where people can feel safe embarking on new thought experiments, bond over inevitable disappointments, and celebrate shared success. Fill it with objects that are engaging and inspiring—a plant, a piece of unusual furniture, something playful. This should be an inspiring space where failure is celebrated as part of the learning process and curiosity flourishes. To nurture fragile new ideas, create a safe harbor to protect them.

Create a space that inspires

If you don't have a dedicated space, improvise: a shared conference room, or even just a wall or an alcove will be a powerful asset for your project. A project space creates a physical reminder of the work. It enables your team to post inspiring imagery and research notes and to be immersed in learning. Visualizing the work being done enables the team to stay on track and remain focused. It supports empathy building, which in turn enables new insights to emerge—the very heart of design.

Make your space flexible, and free up plenty of wall space. Large foam core boards (carried by most art stores and some office supply stores) are an effective aid for visualizing ideas quickly, collaboratively, and flexibly. When not in use, they can be stacked away behind a door and don't take up much room. Tables and chairs that can be folded up and moved around in various configurations will serve you well.

Mood is important: this should feel like a place where you can be relaxed and comfortable. You will be getting out of your mental comfort zones and asking others to get out of theirs, and the space should support this process. Visitors should get an immediate sense that different rules apply here. Arrange the furniture to suit the team and project. Adjust lighting and music to team tastes. This is your team's space: Let them own it! Invent team rituals, so from the moment you start working together, it feels different. Two-minute team yoga? Tea-time? Watering the plant? You'll see what gets your team's energy going.

Supplies

Discovery Design is experiential, visual, and tactile, and having materials like sticky notes and semi-thick permanent markers on hand will encourage your team to work in a different way. Here is a list of essentials we'd recommend you order as a start for your innovation space:

- 50x packs of bright-colored 3"x3" and 3"x5" sticky notes
- 6x white 48" x 96" x 3/8" foam core boards
- 5x boxes of 100 clear push pins
- 6x rolls of cellophane tape
- 5x packs of colored small sticky dots
- 5x packs of 12 black fine point permanent markers
- 5x easel pads—the ones you can stick to a wall
- 1x box of 12 binder clips, small, 3/4"
- 1x scissors
- 500x sheets of white laser paper 8 1/2" x 11" (or A4) and 11" x 17" (or A3)
- Recurring supply of healthy snacks—creative work is thirsty and energetic work!

Scope

Prepare

Discover

Synthesize

Generate

Prototype

Pilot

Spread

Step 2-4 Dot the i's and cross the t's

Address privacy, regulatory, insurance, ethical, resource, and other considerations.

The hospital setting is a high-risk and highly protected environment. And so it should be! Part of the designer's mindset is to empathize with the system and respect the rules that are in place. Before you embark, make sure that you've attended to all of the operational constraints.

Allowing for the vast diversity of today's healthcare institutions, here are some things you may want to check off your list:

Legal, regulatory, and ethical

Consult with your legal, privacy, and compliance departments before proceeding.

- Find out if you or your team needs:
    - Background investigation
    - Health screening
    - Confirmation of qualifications
    - Identification badge
    - General hospital or department orientation/training
- Remember that it can be significantly harder to gain entry for non-employee team members into the care environment. If you are using consultants or external partners, have they been through the necessary onboarding process? Do you have appropriate contracts and business associates agreements in place? Do the contracts sufficiently detail the kinds of activities they will be conducting?
- Is the subject matter of your project regulated, for example, by the U.S. Food and Drug Administration (FDA) or Department of Health and Human Services? (HHS). If you're not sure, ask your compliance office. Are your project activities subject to or sanctioned under healthcare privacy laws? Do you need to consult with your Institutional Review Board (IRB)?
- Make sure any recording devices and data sharing technology are approved by your institution.

Political

- Have you engaged all of the necessary groups and stakeholders before you begin?
- Is any other group responsible for the space you will be using? You may not need to engage everyone upfront, but make sure you know the players. Take advice from your executive sponsors and partners.

Participants

The people you will be working with exist in a highly regulated and operationally constrained environment.

- If your team or participants include unionized staff, you must understand and work with any requirements laid down by the union, such as when and where you can meet and what compensation you can offer. Be proactive in engaging with union representatives and explain that improving the healthcare environment is in everybody's interest. There may not be a precedent for this kind of work.

- Sometimes participants are "volunteered" by their leadership and may not understand your aims or be comfortable with the process. Take the time to communicate what you are doing and make it clear that you are not coming to assess their work or performance, but seeking inspiration.

- Take account of shift schedules for clinical staff, ward rounding times, training requirements. Are people on your project because they need to complete an improvement project? What is the deadline for them? How might job rotations affect team member and participate availability?

Dress

The right attire shows that you are culturally appropriate and helps to dismantle hierarchies when it's needed.

- If you are presenting in front of executives, it's best to wear business attire.

- If you are shadowing nurses and clinicians in the care environment, wear business attire or scrubs as appropriate; leave jewelry and perfumes behind.

- Make sure the team remembers infection control requirements including gloves, masks, caps, face shields, etc.

- Avoid overdressing for any conversations. You want to put your participants at ease, and anything that connotes hierarchy may undermine your efforts.

Step 2-5 Host a team kickoff

Rally your team, discuss the calendar, share what you know.

Get your project off to a good start with a solid kickoff strategy (you may need more than one as each layer of team charts its particular path). Craft your kickoff experiences around two goals: to enable people to connect both on a personal level and as a team, and to align team members around basic project content and logistics.

Running the team kickoff

These are the ingredients we use for hosting successful team kickoffs:

Ice-breaker

Prior to the meeting, send each participant a "homework" question relating the challenge to something genuinely personal. This is a great way to break the ice and learn about people's personal styles, passions, and life outside work. It sets a tone that is open, personal, and engaging, and sparks inspiration from the very first moments of the project.

Ask participants to prepare a story of something in their personal life that was really frustrating until they figured out how to fix it, and to present it in the form of a two-minute story for the group (along with a photo or object that represents it). For example, it could be something about household chores, their daily commute, a family vacation, and so on.

Questions to consider include:

1. What was the process of coming up with the solution?
2. Who was involved?
3. What worked, and why did it work?
4. How has the change been sustained?
5. How has this changed their relationship with the people involved in the process?

Team introductions

Give each person five minutes to share something about his or her role in the organization, background, motivations, and personal goals for the project. As they speak, ask everyone to jot down key phrases or quotes that stand out to them (sticky notes are always useful to have around). Share those notes with the group after each introduction, and post them on a foam core board. This is also a good way of getting folks in the habit of using sticky notes!

Story:

It's day one of a new project: the kickoff workshop in a highly technical field. Process managers, key opinion leaders, and expert practitioners are coming together to ensure we get off to a good start.

As is our habit, we had prepared homework. Each participant had been asked to bring in an object that was personally important to him or her: a publication, a tool, and, in one case, a device he had invented. The atmosphere quickly became a hot house of intellectual competition.

When his turn comes, one team leader, with a doctorate in engineering from a distinguished German university, awkwardly pulls out a smooth, polished stone from his pocket: "My son gave this to me many years ago. I carry it to remind me why I do this work and what really matters."

In a moment, the atmosphere changes: suddenly everyone is talking about what brought them to the field in unexpectedly personal terms. At last we have the right conditions for creating a team.

Why are we here?

Give a short overview of the design challenge and the design process. Consider giving each member of the team a common reading. For example, you might send them a review article on the problem space.

Review the process you followed in framing the design project. Explain why this project was chosen and the support you received at both the executive and frontline level. Include a clear statement of what you are trying to achieve and why. Anticipate future mission creep by making it clear what the mission is not. Establish both hard and soft "guardrails" and any areas for the project to avoid.

This includes sharing your hopes and expectations about the vibrant culture you want to create in the team. Share the Discovery Design mindsets and ask the team to hold each other accountable to them. Make sure the team has clear expectations regarding team confidentiality and who they can speak to if they have any concerns.

What do we know?

This is a great time to assess your group's knowledge and understanding. Don't be afraid to get into specifics, but beware of the temptation to dive into excessive detail that can derail the agenda and dissipate the energy in the room. Look for open-ended questions—"To whom should we speak?" "What are we trying to learn?"—that feed directly into your research plan.

Make sure that you know what has been done before in this area, both in your own institution and elsewhere, so that you do not waste time or do redundant work. It is one thing to start with a clean slate, but another to reinvent the wheel.

Be aware of efforts that may have been attempted previously or elsewhere, but avoid being drawn into deep analysis of why they didn't work. Trust the process and keep your focus forward.

Share superpowers

A powerful and playful tool for breaking the ice and getting to know one another is the "superpowers" exercise:

1. Give everyone some sticky notes and markers.
2. Ask them to come up with a superpower they think they have and a superpower that they wish they had, and to draw them.
3. Have them report out, and then post their notes to a foam core board.
4. Cluster notes that are thematically similar.
5. Discuss!

Review calendar and team expectations

Talk through the team structure again, and be clear about the specific tasks and the time and commitment required for each phase of the project. Who are the project sponsors? Who is on the core team? Who are the key partners? Are there additional stakeholders that might need to be included?

Talk about people's needs and desires. It's always good to be aware of things like personal space, individual working styles, time management practices, and so on. Review the project calendar and note vacations and potential bottlenecks.

Logistics

Decide how you are going to share information and communicate as a team. If your organization has multiple tools to choose from, such as Slack, Basecamp, or Dropbox, choose the one that works best for your team.

Hopes and fears

People may be uncomfortable talking about their fears, but doing so helps build empathy and trust within the team and emphasizes the value of each person's perspective, which can foster a higher level of engagement later on.

Story:

In a Hopes and Fears exercise, almost everyone worried about the time commitment involved. Arranging meetings together would hard. There was a lot to get done and people had other responsibilities. Hearing this, the project sponsor offered to pull in some extra administrative support—something that hadn't been on the table before.

Here's how it works:

1. Give everyone some sticky notes and a marker, and ask them to list three hopes and three fears in relation to the project.
2. Ask everyone to report out one by one, and to post the sticky notes to a board.
3. Together, cluster sticky notes that are thematically similar.
4. Develop action items to address key goals and barriers.

Sponsors and partners kickoff

Organize a second kickoff meeting, this time including stakeholders, leaders, and key decision makers, as well as your core team.

The goals are similar, but with a greater focus on gathering information from the most expert and senior stakeholders of your project:

- Do they understand and agree with the process and scope?
- Who should the team speak to?
- What outcomes are expected by the end of the current timeline?

One way of thinking of this meeting is that your team is forming a contract with the senior stakeholders: this is what we intend to do with these resources. Do we have your support to commit to this process? If so, this is what we will deliver.

When talking to senior stakeholders we recommend framing the anticipated results of a project as a specific number of the following "outputs":

- Insights—fresh perspective on the challenge, based on primary research (typically 8-10)
- Opportunity areas—system inadequacies, breakdowns, or friction points that, if addressed, would address the challenge directly (typically 3-4)
- Concepts—4-6 ideas that resolve the challenge (or important aspects of it) articulated sufficiently for evaluation

These are explained in more detail in later chapters.

Plan your kickoff meeting

A good kickoff meeting can be a game changer. You can use this checklist to plan yours.

1. Purpose

Generate a statement you can share with invitees that states the purpose of the meeting.

2. What's the endpoint?

This step is to inspire your thinking. By the end of the meeting, what are your personal goals—what do you want to be able to say, do, think, and feel by the end?

Say: ______________

Do: ______________

Think: ______________

Feel: ______________

What do you need to do to accomplish your personal goals for this meeting?

By the end of the meeting, what concrete deliverables do you want to walk away with?

3. Participants

Who will you invite? Who needs to be there? Who should you meet with separately?

By the end of the meeting, what do you want participants to be able to say, do, think, and feel? Think about how you will leverage or respond to their perspectives or questions they might bring to the meeting.

____
Attendee

____
Say, Do, Think, Feel

____
Perspective, Question, Concern

4. The story

Think about the meeting like a movie: Where does it start? How does it flow? Where does it end?
Design your meeting by thinking about the topics you want to cover, the reason for them, how they'll be covered, who will lead them, and for how long.

Topic: ______________

Purpose: ______________

Process: ______________

Time: ______________

Leader: ______________

5. Where

The space you choose will depend on your goals: Should this feel small and intimate? Open and refreshing? Inspire a "wow factor"? Formal and business-like? Do you want to stoke interactivity? Dismantle hierarchies?

Idea 1: ___________

Idea 2: ___________

Idea 3: ___________

6. Homework

Create a short, interactive set of materials that you want people to look at beforehand or prepare to share. A summary of a scientific paper? A YouTube video? A table or graph? A photograph? Ideas:

Idea 1: ___________

Idea 2: ___________

Idea 3: ___________

Idea 4: ___________

7. Agenda

Create and send out a formal agenda including the following elements:

- Project name
- Sponsor and leader
- Meeting title and purpose
- Date
- Location
- Attendees
- List the topics, their purpose, allotted times, and topic leaders.

You have now embarked on a journey that will be rewarding not only to your healthcare improvement team, but also beneficial to your organization, the people who work there, and the patients it serves. You are now ready to go out into the field and meet the people who will be the ultimate beneficiaries of your work.

Discover

"Empathy is about standing in someone else's shoes, feeling with his or her heart, seeing with his or her eyes. Not only is empathy hard to outsource and automate, but it makes the world a better place."

—Daniel H. Pink

Having identified an area of opportunity and prepared for project launch, you are ready to enter the Discover phase. If the previous stages gave you the "what" and the "where," Discovery uncovers the "how" and the "why." This is where an innovation team learns to question its assumptions, widen its perspective, and deepen its insight.

Our goal in Discover is to uncover nuances that may lie concealed in the depths of the problem space and to attain a deeper understanding of the people within it. Assuming a beginner's mindset, your team will build deep empathy with people affected by the problem you plan to address, probe the social and system context, collect inspiration, and learn from experts in your own and adjacent fields. You will explore the connections among hard data, competing mental models, and stories rich with emotion.

Process steps

Step 3-1 Plan your exploration

Identify sources of inspiration and prepare to meet people in real-life contexts.

Step 3-2 Gather inspiration

Learn from users, experts, and secondary research.

Step 3-3 Share stories and learning

Capture and share your learning with your team.

Step 3-4 Host a fieldwork snapshot meeting

Review learning and collect feedback.

Step 3-1 Plan your exploration

Identify sources of inspiration and prepare to meet people in real-life contexts.

In some contexts it can be of benefit to approach a new design challenge with a blank slate. The healthcare environment, however, involves highly specialized units, divergent cultures, vulnerable populations, extensive regulations, and a multiplicity of fluid interactions among people, systems, and technology. There are always opportunities for improvement and innovation, but these must be situated within a framework that is built upon evidence and assures efficacy and safety. It is essential that you enter this environment with a deep understanding of the history, context, and science behind your challenge.

Story

During research in an academic medical center, we realized that conversations and involvement in improvement activities seemed to focus almost entirely on the day shift staff. When we asked about night shift, there seemed to be a general impression that "things were different," but not much clarity about how and why.

The only way of really understanding this other world was to join the night shift. It was immediately clear that specific constraints were different: typically fewer staff members on duty, reduced support (many hospital resources are closed at night), and senior hospital staff were unreachable.

By talking to them about their experiences, we learned how night-shift staff felt distant from improvement work; change was sometimes communicated to them late in a transition process and didn't acknowledge their realities. As a result, there was a negative impression of and resistance to change.

Secondary research

What does the literature say about the common causes and contributing factors to the problem you are working on, and what lessons can be drawn from it? What solutions have others employed? You should read the research—not just review articles—and evaluate the methods used and the subjects studied. Review the literature with the same critical eye you applied to your data in Scope. In addition to the medical literature, be aware that there is much to be learned from such adjacent fields as behavioral economics, human factors and ergonomics, and psychology. Do they discuss situations similar to those you are observing? Are there research-based models you can use to frame your exploration? Have they identified solutions that inspire you?

In-context interviews, observations, and immersion

In Discovery Design, we supplement quantitative data and published research with direct experience. The goal of qualitative, human-centered design research is to gain insight into the people involved with patient care generally and with your design challenge in particular. The best way to do this is to conduct in-context interviews, observe people in their native environments, and create experiences that allow you to immerse yourself in the problem space.

Remember that you are not testing a hypothesis or proving a theory. Instead, lay aside your assumptions and agendas, and explore possibilities you might not have thought about before. We use the word "empathy" to describe the goal of understanding others' experience informationally, but also emotionally. It's not the same as agreeing with their points of view, but being able to identify with how they came to hold them and why they behave in a certain way. The people you speak with should feel your genuine interest in what matters to them.

Design research is illustrative, not definitive; it captures stories, not numbers. We seek inspiration, not validation. We're looking for "moments that matter" in the daily lives of people in patient care settings, and we pay close attention to the relationships between people and people, people and resources, and people and systems. Always remember that the qualitative insights you gather through interviews and observations, because of their nature (anecdotal) and sample size (small) won't prove anything. Nor are they intended to: The purpose of qualitative design research is to reveal underlying meaning and focus our attention on opportunities.

Expert perspectives

Schedule one-on-one sessions to learn from internal or external subject matter experts. You will get the most out of their time by conducting background reading and preparing thoughtful questions in advance. Extend your topics of discussion beyond content expertise: How do ideas move through the organization? What are the successes and failures they've seen? What else should you be thinking about? Can they connect you to others from whom you might learn? Identify the experts, contact them, and see if they will share their thoughts with you.

Analogous experiences

Seeking inspiration from contexts outside your own can lead to fresh insights and new perspectives. Think of situations that might illuminate your challenge from an analogous perspective: What can you learn about an emergency room by observing a restaurant kitchen or a kindergarten playground? The "customer experience" is central to healthcare; how does Disney do it? Or Airbnb? Or Trader Joe's?

Data dive

What other data might be useful for understanding the system for which you are designing? Nursing staff ratios, patient volume, revenue, tests ordered, patient satisfaction surveys, and staff engagement scores might all be useful for understanding the system and the people. Reach out to other departments to see what other measures might be useful. Quantitative data and qualitative research have a push-pull dynamic: data can reveal gaps where research can be helpful, while research can give deeper meaning to data needed for innovation and design.

Story

While investigating the experience of diapering an infant, we wanted to see how other people optimized changing clothes for speed and convenience. For example, the team visited the backstage of a theater to see how people got quickly in and out of their costumes; we then observed how rock climbers got quickly in and out of their gear.

Selecting candidates

Healthcare is complex, and to come up with solutions that work it is necessary to understand the work environments of the people for whom you are designing. Map the inputs and outputs of the system from the perspective of flows and take account of roles and functions within it: patients, staff, nurses, physicians, and others who may be less visible.

Most team members will have a mental model of the systems in which they are working, but these may contain unproven assumptions. Having your team draw their mental models and share them with you early in the project will highlight areas that need more exploration. Use your supply of sticky notes to represent individuals, and roles, and the flow of information, processes, products, and tasks.

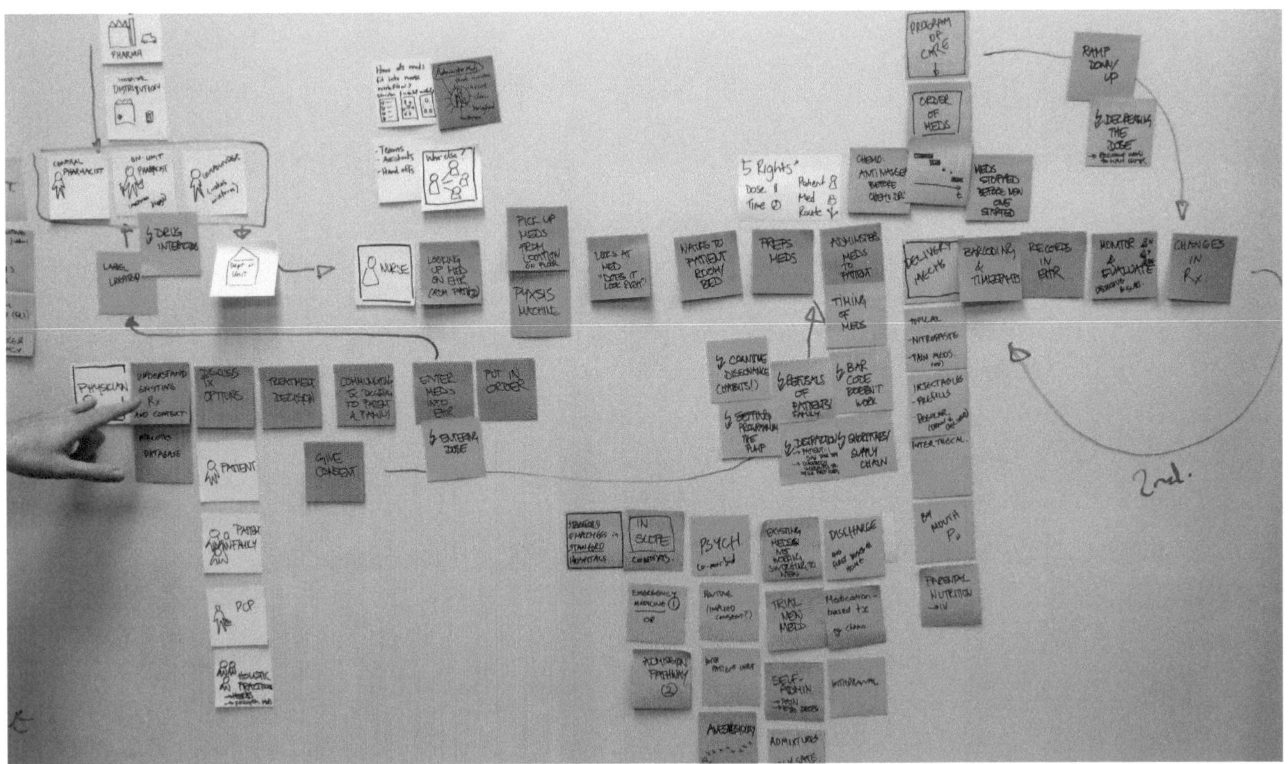

This example shows a map of medication flows through a healthcare organization. It took about 30 minutes to create and facilitated a conversation around project scope and candidate selection.

Your candidates are representatives of unique behavioral segments and groups that have a special story to tell. To begin, try mapping all of the key stakeholders involved in the problem space you are investigating.

For example, the diagram below suggests a field of possible interview candidates for a team hoping to improve the admissions process from a patient point of view:

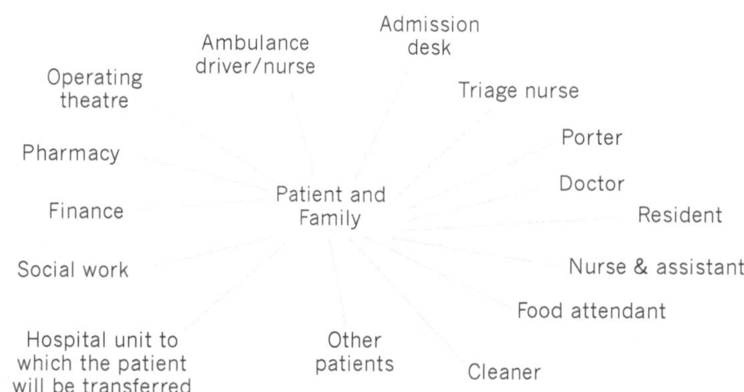

Some of these stakeholders might be directly involved in providing care: physicians and nurses, for example. Others—the pharmacist, the food service worker, the hospital cleaning staff—might be less visible but also have important roles to play. And remember, the person most intimately connected with the patient is…the patient! Always try to include patients and family networks in your research. Their perspective is essential for a complete picture and often contains unique observations and insights no one among the project or healthcare teams will have thought of before.

Ideal candidates

Wherever possible, arrange a short phone conversation with patients, clinicians, administrators, or experts you are thinking of meeting with. You can usually get a good read of their style. The ideal candidate might have some of the following qualities:

- has a unique point of view or experience that is directly relevant
- is naturally talkative and opinionated
- is interested in your agenda, not their own
- is aware of the area related to your challenge
- has witnessed a shift in practice
- has developed own practices/protocols
- is particularly frustrated with the current practices
- has witnessed a reluctance to change
- loves to try out new ideas!

Story

When designing new experiences for lab workers, we looked for people with an extreme fear of needles. This prompted us to ask what changes in environment, tools, roles, and processes might make them more comfortable. The results not only addressed needle safety, but pointed the way to approaches that generally reduced anxiety and stress for all lab workers.

Inspiration from the margins

Interviewing people in the mainstream has value, but findings will likely be incremental due to similarities in their experiences, workflows, and personalities. We therefore seek inspiration also from those at the margins where we are more likely to discover new information and make new connections. These are people on the edges of the spectrum whose needs may be amplified and whose attitudes, behaviors, emotions, and work-arounds may be revealing precisely because they are atypical. And your solutions must work for them as well.

Examples of various interesting or atypical stakeholders include:

- the most experienced and least experienced
- the very young and the very old
- those who break the rules or create work-arounds
- high energy or low energy
- unique use of technology, such as apps or devices
- extreme attitudes toward technology, processes, or tools
- highly motivated patients who care well for themselves vs. patients who need strong guidance

Look for inspiration from users at the margins

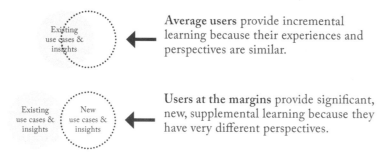

Existing use cases & insights

Average users provide incremental learning because their experiences and perspectives are similar.

Users at the margins provide significant, new, supplemental learning because they have very different perspectives.

You do not have time to interview everyone; therefore, seek inspiration from users at the margins.

How much is enough?

The number of inspiration points you need will vary by project, but in general your focus should be depth over breadth. From the discipline and practice of qualitative research, here are some guidelines you may wish to consider:

- With a thoughtful selection process of people to spend time with, and getting to the level of depth required, you should be able to conduct 2-4 sessions in a good day, or 1-2 clinics or hospital units.
- Shadowing one person for an hour followed by a short interview is likely to be much more productive than "interviewing" four people for 15 minutes each.
- Estimate 45-120 minutes per interview or observation. In addition, after each session you will need to allocate at least 30 minutes for capturing key stories in your notebook or on sticky notes.
- And remember that for every hour spent in conversation or observation, you will need at least an hour to sift through your stories and share them with your core team.
- Leave breathing room between sessions. You'll need to account for travel time, parking, and time to process each session before heading off to the next. If too much is crammed into one day, your interviews will flow into one another, and team members can get mixed up about who said what.

Plan for around eight to sixteen individuals, depending on the size of your design team. A large team (4-5) can handle larger research plans, but for two to three people, ten to twelve participants is sufficient. This speaks to the difference between design and formal medical research. Statistical methods can track meaningful information from larger samples of subjects, but design research is about gathering inspiration from real people and the contexts in which they work. To derive the greatest benefit from your exploration, you need to be able to hold the complete set of relevant information in the "communal brain" of your team.

Recruiting candidates

Recruiting participants is a huge challenge in the healthcare context where schedules are often planned months in advance and given the uncertainties of high patient volumes, staffing constraints, and local, state, and federal requirements. We cannot emphasize this too strongly: Start your recruiting as far in advance as possible.

Tip

When recruiting patients, be mindful of having them opt in with a clear explanation of what will be asked of them if selected.

Sometimes staff may be "voluntold" to be part of your research. Meet with them first, explain what they are being asked to take part in, and give them the option of withdrawing.

For each stakeholder group, prepare a one-half or one-page summary of the project: what, why, who, and when. Explain the context for interviewing them and include that you will keep confidential any identifiable information they have not explicitly permitted you to share. If they don't know you, add a little about yourself: a photo, a short bio, or something about yourself that will break down barriers and minimize intimidation.

It is important to explain that this is not an audit and that your intention is not to measure anyone's performance. "For example, you might wish to tell the group, 'We are here to learn from you because you are the expert. Your own experience will help us to design a better experience for everyone.'"

It can be particularly challenging to gain access to unionized workers such as nurses. You may need to think about how to pay for the additional time that nurses and other staff devote to you. The best strategy may be to work with the Chief Nursing Officer and nurse managers to arrange favorable times to visit their units. Try to experience the nursing environment at both its busiest and quietest times. One might be best for observations; the other might be more suitable for conducting interviews.

Plan your exploration

You're now ready to plan your reserach!

1. List as many sources of inspiration as you can, and circle each that you think would be most productive to your design challenge.
2. List the people who will use the product or system.
3. Include both typical and more marginal candidates

Tip

Plan for success by inviting interviewees to bring a friend or colleague with whom they feel comfortable. Recruiting pairs (dyads) who know each other can create an effective dynamic, but be mindful that the two participants are helping each to open up rather than the opposite. For example, an older patient together with an adult son or daughter caregiver could work well or could be inhibiting. It may be more productive to interview them separately or at different times.

Exploration Guide

Users (ten or more individuals)

PARTICIPANT	DESCRIPTION

Exploration Guide (continued)

Observations (four or more individuals)

LOCATION	LOCATION

Literature

RESOURCE	RESOURCE

Data Sources

RESOURCE	RESOURCE

Experts (five or more individuals)

NAME	DETAILS

Analogous inspiration (three or more locations)

OBSERVATION	RATIONALE FOR SELECTION

Interviewing your candidates

Effective interviews are built upon trust. Begin with introductions in which you set the context, and establish rapport. Once your subject is comfortable, move on to elicit stories that explore emotions, motivations, and choices. Only then are you ready to dig deeper with probing questions.

Here's an excellent visual structure adapted from the work of Michael Barry, design researcher and co-founder of pioneering innovation consultancy Point Forward, that visualizes the journey of an effective interview.

The curve indicates the depth of insights and value of information gathered at different stages during the interview:

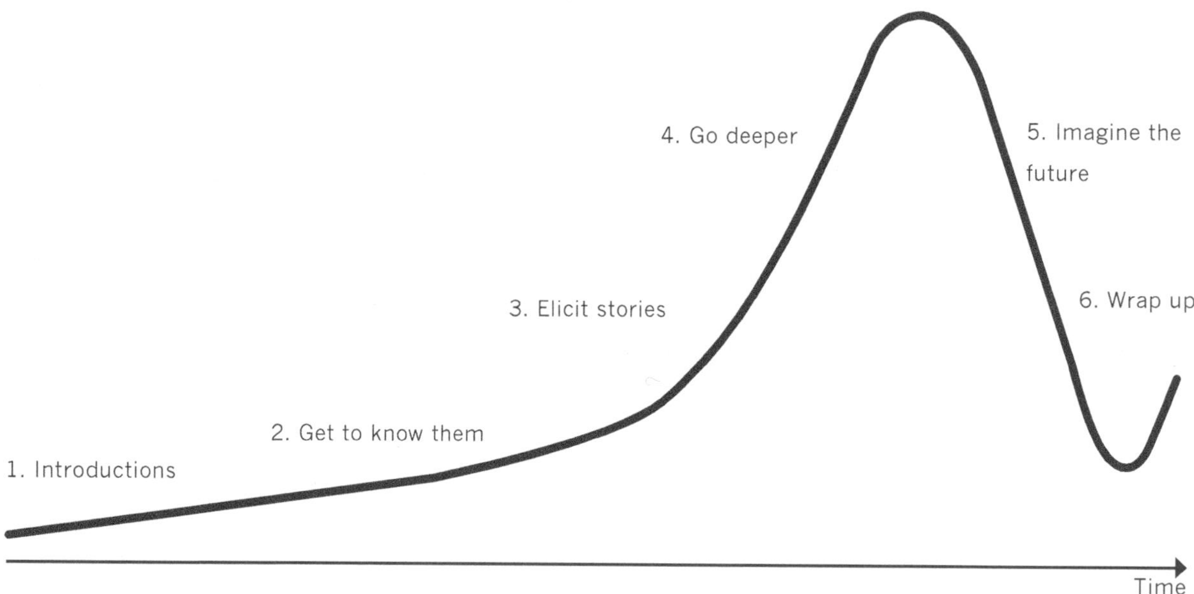

One useful and simple high-level structure is to structure your interview in six parts

Introductions

Make your participant feel comfortable by explaining the goals of your project, setting clear time boundaries for the interview, inviting them to share openly and candidly, and assuring them that any identifiable information they provide will be held in strict confidence by the team.

Get to know them

Give this at least 10 minutes.

Go right to the beginning and start with the basics with open-ended questions: Who are they? How did they choose this career? Where do they live? Even hobbies and pets are good openers. Knowing that someone moved to the USA at age 12 tells you a lot about how they see the world; knowing that she has a one-hour commute home explains why she's in a hurry to leave the hospital at night.

Elicit stories

There are many nested time lines in our lives:

When did you start working here? Where were you before? What was that like? Do you remember the first week that you had this job? What was hard about starting? What changes have you seen in this process? When did they come about and why? How did they impact you? Map these out in your notebook—get visual. If the interviewee is open to it, ask them to draw the timeline.

Go deeper

The richest insights come from understanding the inner world of emotions, motivations, and desires of people. Now it's time to go deeper: How did that make you feel? Are there moments that sap your energy? Tell us, what happened? What brings you joy in your work? Can you tell me a story about that? What are you hoping for?

Imagine the future

At this point you can begin to direct your questions specifically towards your design challenge, but frame them carefully: "How could we improve your situation?" will likely prove unenlightening because most people cannot articulate a better future in the absence of some context. Try a more casual approach: "If you had a magic wand, what is the very first thing you'd change?" Toward the end of the interview you can return to more focused questions.

Wrap up

Thank your interviewees for sharing their ideas and experiences with you, and reiterate that you won't share their information beyond the team without their express permission. Ask them if they'd be open to talking again as the project progresses. As you exit, keep your pen handy: You'd be surprised at the afterthoughts that occur to them as you reach for the door!

Prepare a discussion guide

1. Gather your team and review the outputs of your kickoff meeting, particularly regarding what you know and don't know about the problem space. For each category of interviewee, brainstorm interview topics.
2. Group similar themes of questions, and order them in a way that makes sense for your interview structure.
3. Add the fine detail: How will you introduce yourselves? How will you warm them up to feel comfortable talking with you? How will you guide conversations to learn deeply about their lives and challenges? How will you thank them for their time?
4. Write up interview questions. Your questions should be open ended and designed to elicit stories. Ask people to tell you the whole story and avoid yes/no questions. Go broad to explore their hopes, fears, and desires, and then go deep. Make your discussion guide easy to read and access at a quick glance. Write down your notes on paper, not on a computer or phone.
5. Remember that this is just a guide. It is okay, in fact essential, to follow off-script tangents that come up in conversation that spark your interest and are relevant to the project.

Tip

- Ask people to tell stories.
- Follow interesting tangents.
- Ask people to show, not just tell.
- Use active listening, clarify if needed.
- Do not react too strongly to their responses, i.e., be unshockable but empathic.
- Don't take sides and get involved in politics; some people will have axes to grind!
- Don't be afraid of pauses.
- Become a visual note taker.
- Write down what inspired you immediately after the session, even if you don't yet know why.
- Be respectful of their time. If the interview is going long, be sure to ask their permission.

Your discussion guide

Get to know them

Introductions: "We are ___." "Please tell us a bit about you, your job, and things you love to do...." Begin to prompt for details of stories and ask "why?" "How come?" "Tell me more about that," etc., to probe deeper even in your initial warmup. This will set the tone for how you expect the conversation and the interaction to go.

Elicit stories

Open up the conversation: "Tell us a story about your experiences...best/worst/memorable?"

Go deeper

What are some questions that can help you understand the user's needs, hopes, and fears? "Why was that particularly hard on that occasion?" "What did we not ask that you were expecting?"

Imagine the future

Specific questions that go direct to your project. "What would have been your ideal experience?" "If you had a magic wand, how would you...?" "What else would you want us to know?"

Wrap up

"We greatly appreciate you telling us about your experiences. We won't share your information or photos beyond the team unless you've given permission. We will tell your story in an anonymous way. Would you be open to talking again as the project progresses? Your insights will help us. Thank you."

Example of a discussion guide for medication safety

Here is the text from a discussion guide we used for a project concerning nursing medication administration safety. What would you keep? What would you do differently?

We typically write up such discussion guides to have many themes in mind, but once we meet a recruit in person, we put this away, try to let the conversation flow, and encourage the participant to talk and guide us to what is most important. Plan, plan, plan, then throw the plan away.

Example discussion guide

Warm ups and context
"We are improvement staff from the hospital, working on a medication safety project. We're looking to understand your experience as a ______ to learn and be inspired." "Everything you say to us will be de-identified and kept strictly confidential." "We will take a few photos along the way today as visual note taking. They are all non-identifiable, for confidential use only within our project, and you will have an opportunity to review them all at the end of our conversation."

"Tell us a little bit about yourself. How/Why did you choose to become...?" "Why do you do what you do?" "What's your superpower?" "Tell us about a typical day/shift."

"Please give us a tour of the places and spaces that you work." In-context tours are very effective. It gets you both up and moving in a natural way, storytelling with props and prompts rather than simply from memory.

"What/where is your favorite part of the day? What is most challenging? What pressures does it have? What rewards? Why?" "How do your energy levels change through the day/week? What/when is energizing? What is draining? Why?" "Tell us a story about when you felt very confident and successful in your work." "When else do you feel confident and successful?" "Please think of a time recently when you felt nervous." "What situations make you feel nervous?"

Culture, Relationships, and Communication
"How do you describe the culture of your team?" "What is your team's personality?" "Tell us about a situation when communication was fantastic and felt great. What happened? Why?" "What tools do you use for communication?" "What style, mode, or personality do you have with different people you work with?" "When do you feel the most flow of great

Tip

1. Brainstorm themes likely to bubble up in your interviews and observations.
2. Capture these high level themes (if studying an ER, for example, "coordination under pressure").
3. Look for other contexts in which these themes manifest, such as an airport or fire station.
4. Look for novel ways the theme is being addressed in this analogous context.
5. Try translating those approaches back to your design challenge ("What if we did xyz in the ER?").

teamwork?" "...And tell us about a time when communication broke down. What happened? Why?" "Can you tell us your point of view about hierarchies in your team? When is this helpful? Not helpful? Why?" "Can you tell us your point of view about gender in the workplace from your experience?" "Please tell us about family and patient involvement that you encounter." "What support or roadblocks do they provide?" "Tell us about a great relationship you've had with a patient and their family" "...what about one that was challenging." "What tips do you have about creating and maintaining these relationships?"

Patient safety culture
"What comes to your mind when you hear the topic of a culture of patient safety?" "What does that mean to you?" "Tell us a story of when you felt very confident in patient safety—yourself or your team. What are the characteristics of that scenario? What brings you ultimate confidence?" "What makes you feel confident that you are accurate?" "What brings you a feeling of solid patient safety? Why?" "What are the characteristics of error-prone situations or people?" "How confident are you that you/your team won't make a mistake in the next 6 months?" "...what about your team, your organization, your profession?" "When do you feel alone?" "What makes you feel safe to speak up if something goes wrong?"

Thought processes during situations
"Please tell us a story of a moment things were not going as planned, for example: 1) things fall out of control entirely (e.g., patient crashes), and you have no exact procedure for what is happening now; 2) you accidentally miss a step because you're moving too fast; and 3) you deliberately skip a step, or 'stretch' a procedure (i.e. "I'll double check it in a few minutes") "When something doesn't go right, what happens next?" "Tell us about the five rights. When are they just not applicable?" "Tell me what you've done when a medication wasn't immediately available."

Attention and awareness
"What is your single biggest distraction?" "If you had a magic wand, what single biggest distraction would you wave away?" "What's the difference between distraction and interruption?" "How do you maintain attention and awareness of all the details of a patient situation?" "Take us there: You are at the workstation on wheels with the red light on. What happens next?" "How do you 'tune out' to keep focus? What is being tuned out?" "How do you deal with fatigue? How do others deal (or not) deal with it?"

Your medication management process
"Tell us about medication management in your day-to-day job." "Please show us your typical medication management process here. What is your usual administration routine for medication?" "What do you focus on the most when managing meds? Why?" "What makes you change this routine?" "What does a more complicated/tricky example look like? Please show us." "How does medication management fit into your other responsibilities?" "How has your process changed over time?" "How is your process for administering

medication different than your peers?" "What are examples of medication administration not going smoothly?" "What are all the different reasons for medication management to go wrong? Where are you or others most likely to make a mistake?" "Help us tease out 'drug side effects' vs 'error' vs. 'harm.'" "When is an 'error' to a layman not an 'error' to a professional?" "How does this differ between clinicians? Between doctors and nurses?" "We'd love to dig into a few specific examples. Could you tell us about a story about when you couldn't find a nurse to do a double check?" "How do you know the drug you are giving is the right drug?" "How much of what you do on a daily basis is covered by specific procedures that you have been taught?" "Do the processes that you are taught accurately reflect how things happen in the real world?" "When do you have to use your personal judgment?" "It seems like there are a lot of overlapping specific step-by-step processes that you have to have in your head (behavior, procedure, cultural). How do you manage all this information?" "How much becomes instinct, and how much is step-by-step rote? In thinking about teaching a new nurse, at what points in the flow of your expertise do the details drop out, as things become second nature?"

Medication safety and errors
"What are the typical pitfalls that you've seen or experienced with medication safety?" "What team or cultural norms are in place to reduce error? The things teams or individuals do, for example, pilots and co-pilots in Australia use humor to keep their relationship more open to talk about problems readily." "We'd love to dig into a few specific examples". "What moments tend to create error: High-alert drugs, double-check drugs/emergencies/displaced/rotating clinicians/family interfering/special times (nights, weekends, shift change, med hour)/interfaces, tools, systems/information overload, fatigue/staff education" "Please tell us a story about a challenging math calculation." Norms/tools/processes/drug infusion pumps: ."Tell me about a time that you had a challenge programming an infusion pump. What did you do? Who did or did not assist? What happened next?"/What are the 'sacred spaces'? How are they respected/not? Why? Why not?" (For example: vests, boxes painted on the floor, red light on WOW)/Feeling on auto-pilot—"When handling drugs with specific checklists (for example vasopressors, bags, and pumps), how do you keep your mind from turning off and just running the checklist?"

Reporting
Here's a tricky topic that we know has many layers. "We'd like to know more about the ins and out of reporting errors and pointing out errors of others." "What's your thought process on deciding what gets reported? What doesn't need to be reported?" "When do you point out errors of others? How? Why? Why not?" "What happens after an error is reported? What does that process feel like?" "When do you or others not report errors? Why?" "What are the ins and outs of near misses?" "Which errors and near misses have you seen that haunt you?"

"Facts bring us to knowledge; stories bring us to wisdom."

—Rachel Naomi Remen

Process change
"We'd like to help improve patient safety. Your insights from our conversation are giving us many ideas! In order to bring these ideas to life, we would like to understand how new ideas and change happen in your team." "Tell us a story about a recent trigger for a change in something that you do." "...What about a trigger for a change in your team, your organization, your profession?" "How do you work with travelers and contractors to help them with the nuance of your procedure process and culture?" "What are the hurdles and challenges to process improvements?" "What incentives do individuals have to drive fixes or process improvements?" "How are disagreements dealt with?" (Clinical disagreements and otherwise) "What's been tried in the past to prevent medication errors?"

Wrap up and thank you
Provide a small thank you gift if appropriate, for example, a meal voucher or small gift card for a patient.

Provide contact info for any follow-up questions or comments.

Tip

As you conduct your interview, be a "learn it all." No question is too big, small, or silly. Stay curious and take lots of photos to document your learning. Photos can be better reminders of what your user has shared than scribbles in your notebook—just be sure to use notate the images afterwards. Don't forget to use an approved camera and scrub your images of any user or patient identifiers!

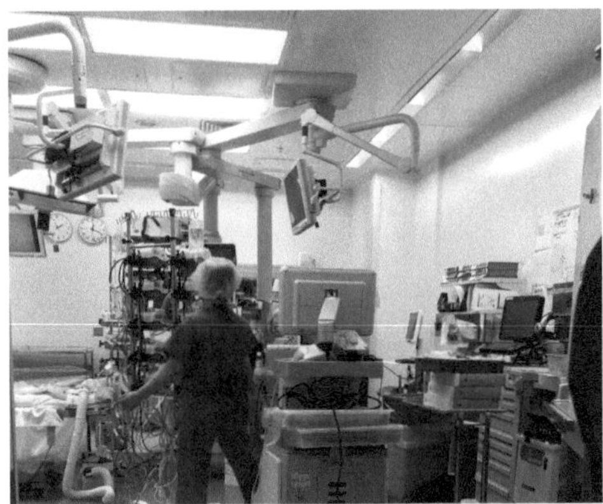

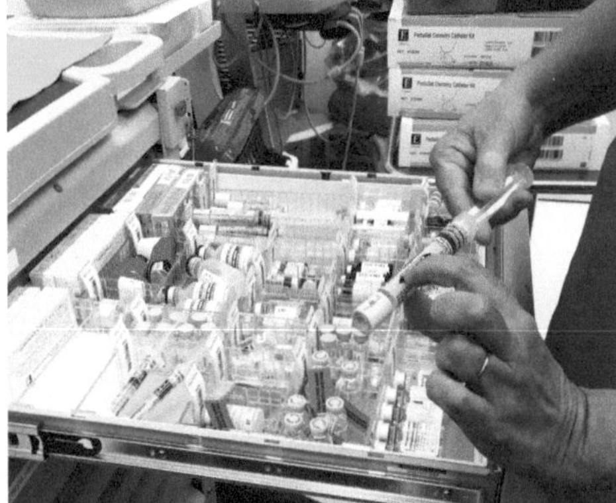

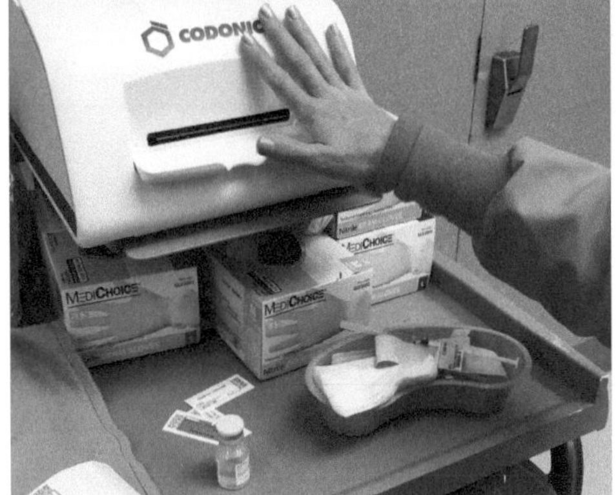

Scope

Prepare

Discover

Synthesize

Generate

Prototype

Pilot

Spread

Step 3-2 Gather inspiration

Learn from users, experts, and secondary research.

The goal of in-context, qualitative research is to uncover implicit needs, hidden challenges, and mental models that underlie the challenge you have identified. You are not looking to prove your data correct but to uncover the layers of meaning behind the data. These are conversations more than interviews. You will find yourself in a unique mode of interaction where interviewees feel they've just had a wonderful conversation.

We conduct observations and interviews in real contexts in order to learn more and faster. Design research allows us to see with our own eyes, ask about things we don't understand, test our assumptions. A skilled interviewer will see behaviors that are difficult to articulate and identify tensions between what people do and what they say. These are often the spaces where design opportunities reveal themselves.

Story 1

While performing a cardiac implant procedure, we noted that surgeons did something that none of them had mentioned in prior interviews: Immediately after opening the packaging they removed an adapter that connected the heart valve to the handle, which disabled a safety shield that protected the delicate valve during implantation. They explained that "the holder is in the way of the final suturing step, so we take it off." This led the design team to reimagine a new holder, handle, and process that drastically reduced the incidence of valve damage and improved market share.

Story 2

Nurses have all sorts of tips, tricks, and workarounds that they develop over time. Pediatric anesthetists each have unique ways that they mark their drugs. However, when we asked where they learned these things they all said that they made the trick up themselves. We then finally asked: "Have you ever shared a tip like this?" The answer was, "No, it would be boastful and presumptive to tell others what to do."

Story 3

A device company found that the owners of its tracker were actively using the device during an initial honeymoon period, but only a very few continued. The design team went out to meet the users who were still using the device and discovered that those people were typically managing more critical health issues (pain, injury), and were therefore more motivated to test it. The team also discovered that there was a difference in the reasons people were wearing the device: Men tended to wear it closer to the hips because of lower back pain, while women tended to wear the device higher to correct shoulder posture. From these insights, the company changed the form factor of the device from a belt to a jewelery pin.

Conducting observations

Select the environments that may be relevant to your design challenge, and secure access, permissions, as well as such things as immunizations. Think about the levels of experience you wish to capture, and familiarize yourself in advance with the layout, inhabitants, and sensitivities of the environment you will be entering. Bring a small notebook only—no laptops. Cameras may or may not be appropriate. If they are allowed, turn off all beeps, flash, and be discreet and attentive to HIPAA issues. If cameras are not permitted, sketch!

Leave at least a few days in your research schedule for serendipity; every project deserving of attention has it, and unexpected developments may reveal valuable opportunities—for example, meeting "hidden" stakeholders that no one had considered. You'll need to find the right balance between maintaining your focus and following a promising hunch.

Tips for observations

Wear comfortable shoes. Expect to be standing on your feet for a long time.

As you introduce yourselves and your project, be respectful of medical staff in tone and manner. This is their home and you are their guests. Your hosts will likely appreciate that you are observing them with the goal of improving their work, but be conscious of patient care activities. Watch and imitate what others do.

Be discreet, so that no one has to pay any attention to you. If you are asked to leave a room because a family needs it, leave. If an ER physician needs the elevator, wait and take the next one. If a nurse needs to administer meds while you are talking with a patient, come back later. Be aware of your body in hallways and anywhere you may brush up against something sterile. Stay out of the way.

Regardless of your seniority and experience, when you are on observations it's important to recognize that you are not the priority now. You need your participants to be as relaxed, natural, and open as possible.

If you use a camera, make sure you have permission and that the flash is off. It is of the utmost importance to be aware of privacy concerns and not to take photos of anything that is identifiable.

What not to photograph: faces, name tags, tattoos (invite participants to cover if possible), unique jewelry (invite to take off for the photos), pill bottles that may have a name on them, paper files and documents on a desk, records on a screen. Have sticky notes handy to cover up before taking a photo.

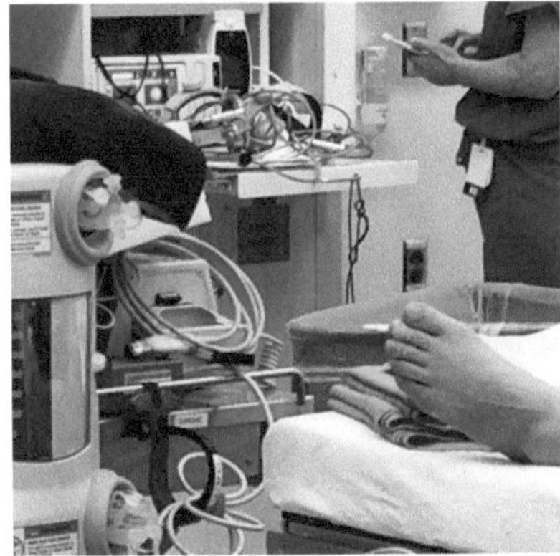

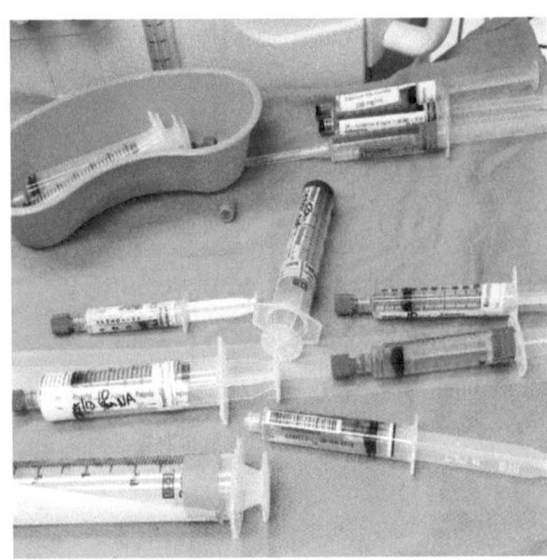

Observe and capture diverse people, environments, and activities. To understand communication flows between stakeholders, we spent time with anesthesiologists, pharmacists, and nurses.

Capturing observations: What? How? Why?

A simple way of cataloguing your observations and drawing insights from them is to use a "What-How-Why" matrix.

1. Prepare: Divide a sheet into three sections: What? | How? | Why?
2. Describe: What? Start with your concrete observations. What was the person doing in your observation or photo? Notice the details of their actions. Try to be objective and not to make assumptions.
3. Understand: How? Describe how the person in the photo or sketch is doing what you observed. Does it look effortful? How quickly are they moving? Where do they pause? What emotions are revealed?
4. Interpret: Why? Why is the person doing what you're observing, in the way you understand it? Here, you'll need to infer emotions, motivations, needs, and aspirations. It's okay if you aren't sure. Be bold. Step out on a limb, and make an inference.
5. Verify: Seek more detail to support or dismiss the inference (if possible) by speaking later with the person or someone else who might know, such as one of their colleagues.

This exercise will help you to uncover unexpected insights that you can test with your team, and that may lead to exciting opportunities for design. Here is an example with notes taken during the observation; naturally yours will be handwritten:

What?

- Nurse preparing meds by the patient's bedside.
- Patient interrupted to ask nurse to clear away milk. Said, "It's been there since last night!" Nurse stops preparing meds and cleared away milk.

How?

- Nurse looks deep in concentration. Performing math? Tried not interrupting flow. Frowned at screen then turned, smiled at patient, and cleared milk.

Why?

- Patients don't understand when they can ask questions.
- Nurses have to switch between clinical and housekeeping modes.
- Prioritizing patient requests brings feeling of being a good nurse, is often cited in patient satisfaction.
- Nurses don't have a good way to signal "I'm available."
- Nurses are readily distracted at all times; during meds time is no exception.

Story

What people say they do and what they actually do can be very different things. A design team interviewed several nurses on a patient-clinician violence-reduction project in a psychiatric hospital. One new nurse explained that he thought they needed more training in de-escalation skills, whereas another nurse, with 30 years of experience, dismissed this idea, pointing out the endless hours spent each day engaged in the practice. Shortly after the conversation the team observed a developing situation on the ward. A patient had become noticeably agitated and was starting to issue threats. The more experienced nurse quickly stepped in to defuse the situation. She used the "right words;" however, her body language and non-verbal communication served to enflame the situation. Reflecting on the incident later it occurred to the team how such strongly expressed views are often rooted in a narrow frame of reference, whereas the opportunity to just sit and observe had yielded far more valuable insights.

Give your mind a rest

Take on a reasonable number of observations per day with your team. It can be tempting to schedule additional sessions, but your priority should be on capturing stories you heard while they are fresh. Allow the details of your observations to soak in. Share. Eat well. Rest your mind. Refresh yourself for the next day.

Conducting interviews

Logistics

Prepare your interview guide, and practice your questions in advance. Take notes in a small notebook and not on a laptop to maintain good rapport. A good rule of thumb is two 90-minute observations or interviews per day. This accounts for time to download and transit. No more than three people should attend any single interview so as not to overwhelm the participant, and each of them should be assigned a clear role. Let one person lead the interview, while the others take notes. If you feel it's appropriate, set aside 10-15 minutes at the end for others on your team to ask about things they're curious about. This is a good way for the whole team to feel invested in more controlled or formal interviews.

In context is best

Spending one-on-one time with your interviewee in his or her own domain is the best way to engage with them, show respect for their expertise, build trust, and gain a rich understanding of their thoughts, emotions, and experiences. It allows them to show you artifacts, tools, and processes they might refer to during your interview. In context also provides a powerful associative prompt for the thoughts, feelings, and emotions your user experiences day-to-day. Ask for permission to take photographs of key spaces, artifacts, and actions, especially anything that might bring an important story to life.

> "Know thy user, and you are not thy user."
>
> —Arnie Lund

Interviewing Experts

If you are interviewing experts or key opinion leaders (KOLs), prepare questions that show you have done some research on their field, but still have much to learn. Don't be afraid of seeming naive; they don't expect you to have their level of expertise. Leverage their knowledge by asking about the patterns they see in the overarching system, industry trends affecting their work, and how their perspective has evolved over time. You may mention you have some knowledge of their field already, but would like to use this time to gain higher-level understanding. Make sure more seasoned researchers are doing expert interviews because there is greater probability that the expert may become a valuable advocate of the work later on.

Tips for effective interviewing:

- Capture what you see and hear as exactly as you can. Capture literal, direct quotes. Try to separate your observations from your interpretations.
- Try to make the interview as friendly and comfortable as possible. Gather stories. Don't push your guest to answer any questions they are uncomfortable with. Ask "why" and "tell me more" as often as you can. Encourage your user to show you as well as tell you.
- Be aware of body language and emotional cues. Look for inconsistencies between what people say and what they do, and notice work arounds and the unusual ways of doing things people have created to do their work. They are often opportunities for inspiration.
- Listen patiently. Do not interrupt. Don't be afraid of silence. We can so often feel the need to ask another question or fill in the space with an explanation when there is a pause. Let your users interpret your question and answer in their own time.
- Avoid the temptation to demonstrate your own knowledge. Even if you know the situation well, let your participant describe it in their own words. Instead of being a "know it all," become a "learn it all." Feel free to ask the same naive questions of different people; you'll surprised at the different perspectives you'll hear.

Dig deeper with a journey map

A journey map is a projective tool for probing deeper into the emotional experience of your interview subject. It can be useful for drawing out the emotions and thought processes that motivate behavior, cause stress, and generate opportunities that might otherwise remain hidden.

The journey map can be used to record a day, a communication, a key process or protocol, a task, or an activity, or to recount an important event, for example, a surgical error.

The journey map below helped a nurse describe her experience in caring for patients in a crowded infusion center. "So often we don't know where the meds are. This is where I feel the most frustration—like on this card here [points at a football player]. It doesn't feel like we and pharmacy are a team. But we just live with it and do our best." Using the same exercise with pharmacists, we discovered they felt the same way! The exercise helped build empathy between stakeholders and revealed a real opportunity for design.

1. Prepare

Print images of a range of modes, emotions, and behaviors. Prepare a page of circles and ask your interviewees to populate it with faces showing emotions such as joy, worry, pride, annoyance, surprise, apprehension, anger, or interest.

2. Draw and extend

Ask your subject to draw the journey on a piece of paper, representing time on the x-axis, and to note key activities and moments along the way. You can give them start and end points for the journey, or better yet, let them mark their own end points.

3. Map several layers deep

Ask your interviewees to map their mood on the y-axis and to assign people and emotion cards to moments along the way; this will bring details and richness to the story. In the previously mentioned example of a medication error, "What were the characteristics of each team member in the time before the procedure, during the error process, and in the aftermath of the error? Where were you most surprised? Worried?" Often people will begin by pointing out the happy or proud success moments. Using the visual cards allows them to share a challenging emotion without having to find words for it.

Story

A journey map can help uncover hidden gaps, emotions, and bottlenecks that interviewees may not be able to remember or express. In one project, an interventional cardiologist said he felt "neutral" during the entirety of a stent procedure, but when asked, "when do you feel this, or this [referring to a worried or angry face sticker]?" he was able to point to several tricky parts of the procedure, which opened up opportunities for design. Reflecting on the exercise, the cardiologist stated, "We're not really allowed to feel emotions – we're expected to be always calm and cool-headed. But this helped me express where the difficulties are."

4. Continue to ask why, follow threads of conversation, and be curious to this individual's experience

Story

In research for a project to design a next-gen gene sequencer, we found that engineers had focused their efforts on optimizing one critical step of the sequencer—but that was much further down the sequencing process than any of us had thought: any errors in the chemistry made earlier would then just be be amplified in the "optimized" phase. On the same project we found that a lot of time was lost when the sequencer got stuck and there was no-one there to see it, especially if they had gone home to let it "work all night." A simple text message system could rescue a night's work if the machine stopped sequencing.

Tip

Use different colors of sticky notes for these categories:

1. Themes that are bubbling up (one or two words, such as "Trust").
2. Observations and Quotes you collected related to a theme (all one color).
3. Insights that summarize the stories (often tensions or shifts).
4. Opportunity Areas, which note potential directions for design.
5. Specific Ideas

Capture your learning

Immediately following your observation, take time to capture the details you found most interesting and write them on sticky notes so you will be able to organize them later. Consider using different colors for observations, quotes, processes, and follow-up items.

Find a space where you can sit with the team and share notes and stories (a coffee shop is fine; driving back from an interview is great). Build on each other's thoughts and allow for multiple (sometimes conflicting) interpretations of what you saw and heard. There is never just a single way of interpreting complex situations.

Capture field notes

As you interview or observe, capture what you are seeing and hearing, especially direct quotes and stories. Separate observations and interpretations. Look for work arounds.

Field Notes

Interviewee	
NAME	LOCATION

QUOTES & OBSERVATIONS	INTERPRETATION

Step 3-3 Share stories and learning

Capture and share your learning with your team.

Now that you have met with your candidates, collected a wealth of quotes, facts and figures, and downloaded your photographs, what do you do with it all? Discovery Design is a collaborative sense-making enterprise, so the next step is to share your learning with your team. Doing so creates a shared body of knowledge, perspectives, and insights from which to begin the task of transforming a mass of information into actionable design.

Share stories

Immediately after each interview, observation, or immersion experience, bring your group together for a downloading session. Each session should take about 30 minutes and should take place within a day or two of your primary research.

1. Gaps. First, review the people you met and the places you visited. Are there any gaps that need to be filled?

2. Moments. Each person in your team should then identify the most important moments they saw, heard, or otherwise inferred from their research. Sticky notes are ideal, but team members should also print photographs. Even thumbnail images serve the purpose of jogging the memory for the team and prompting richer stories.

3. Stories. Take turns sharing stories about what you have learned. Topics should include personal details, interesting stories, and observations about what was most memorable or surprising. Don't worry if details might not seem relevant at this point; it could prove to illuminate an interesting pattern.

4. Synthesize. When you have finished, coordinate your sticky notes (by color, if possible). Look for evidence of motivations (What did your subject care about?); barriers (What most frustrated him or her?), and interactions (How did your user interact with his or her environment?). Once your team has collated this mass of "raw" data, you are ready to Capture insights, Reflect on their possible meaning, and Cluster them into meaningful patterns or categories. Headline each of these categories with a memorable caption.

In this story sharing session, the team included an anesthesiologist, an improvement scientist, a frontline nurse, a nurse practitioner, a senior administrator, and a risk manager. Each person viewed the learning through a unique lens, which helped frame the challenge from a system-wide perspective.

From empathy to insight

An empathy map is a powerful device for drawing out insights from your interviews and observations, and developing a Point of View (PoV) statement that defines the opportunity for design. A PoV takes your understanding of the insights you have generated and defines an actionable design opportunity that is specific to the population you are hoping to serve.

Creating an empathy map

It's possible to create a composite empathy map for the users you spoke to and observations you made. To create an Empathy Map, divide an easel pad into the following quadrants:

SAY:

What are some important or memorable quotes and defining words your user said?

THINK:

Infer what you think your user was thinking. What beliefs might they have?

DO:

What behaviors and actions did you observe or notice that stood out?

FEEL:

What do you think your interviewee was feeling?.

Populate each quadrant with photographs, anecdotes, and notes from your fieldwork. Some of this will require inference, interpretation, and outright speculation.

Consider the following examples:

"A new nurse [subject] needs a better way to ask questions about patient care [subject's need], because the fear of embarrassment is more powerful than the fear of making an error [Surprising insight]."

"Professional hospital pharmacists [subject] need a better way of getting feedback about their services [subjects' need] because the system does not allow for direct contact with other clinicians or patients [surprising insight]."

Creating a point of view statement

Once you have your empathy map, we can then generate a PoV statement using this formula:

"**[Subject]** needs a way to **[subject's need]**, because **[surprising insight]**."

[Subject]: Describe your target group in illustrative, emotive terms.

[Subject's need]: Based on what you've learned from your empathy map, what emotional, physical, or practical needs do your users have? Frame needs as verbs rather than nouns. Verbs ("Nurses need a way to [do, feel, access, etc.]") are more generative and point to more varied solutions than nouns ("Nurses need a new [thing, device, technology, process, etc.]"), which often contain an assumption about what the solution should be.

[Surprising insight]: Insights should not simply be the reason for the need, but a synthesized statement that emotes and inspires the demand for a solution. Insights often grow from tensions and contradictions you might have observed or perceived, or from asking "why" in the face of an unusual work around or behavior. Keep asking "why" until you get to the core motivation.

This is an empathy map we generated from shadowing a young surgeon on a project in which we were looking for ways to improve safety in the operating room.

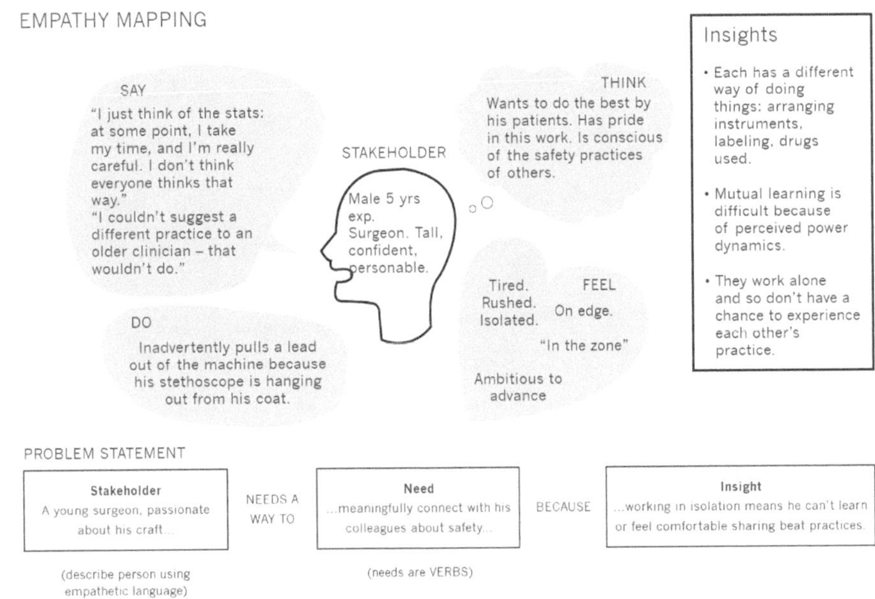

Create an empathy map

Using sticky notes and foam core boards, capture key snippets here:

SAY
Quotes and defining words

Place sticky note here

THINK
Thoughts and beliefs

Place sticky note here

DO
Actions and behaviors

Place sticky note here

FEEL
Feelings and emotions

Place sticky note here

USER NEEDS

Place sticky note here

INSIGHTS

Place sticky note here

POINT OF VIEW STATEMENTS

Your point of view statements create a powerful roundup of what you've learned that can now be used to go back to your stakeholder audiences and gather feedback. Are you on the right track? Have you discovered something new?

Step 3-4 Host a fieldwork snapshot meeting

Review learning and collect feedback.

By this point you have amassed a huge amount of learning and are beginning to form some initial ideas about where the ripest opportunities for innovation and improvement lie. However, before jumping into the formal work of Synthesize (next phase), you will need to test your assumptions and invite feedback from the prospective beneficiaries of your work through a Fieldwork Snapshot Meeting. This is an opportunity to validate your findings, especially when venturing into specialized areas of which you may have only partial understanding. Such discussion also helps nurture ownership of the problem, proposed solutions, and the process required to bring about the desired change. It will also help you to find out if there are any big gaps in your fieldwork. Did you discover a hidden stakeholder group that needs additional field time?

You should also pause to assess your team's mood. Everyone's minds will by this point be full of stories, and connective threads will be forming. But in general, the team may feel unsure where it is headed. This is as it should be. If you know all the answers at this point then you have not gone deep enough. There will be a lot more wrangling with this thick data from this point forward, but your team should feel at least a few strong points, even if not sure what to do with them.

Conduct a fieldwork snapshot

Tip

Create an "Idea Wall" to capture ideas that happen to come up. This will help people feel heard, captures spontaneous ideas, and helps to keep the conversation on track with the story sharing. "Great, thanks, we got that idea! Now, back to Liz in the OR..."

1. Create a foam core board that represents each area of research. You may have a composite board for nurses that you interviewed, an expert interviews board, a secondary research board, analogous inspiration, and so forth.
2. Cluster stories into common themes or patterns that you have observed. Try phrasing simple themes as an insight. Your boards could be arranged as follows:

   AREA - Where did you go? Who did you interview/observe? Include any observations of what you found particularly interesting about that particular area.

   INSIGHTS - a clear statement that highlights a unique user need or challenge. Include top, juicy user quotes and photos (usually choose the most compelling two to three quotes and pictures).

   OPPORTUNITIES - three to five Opportunity Statements: "How might we..."

   QUESTIONS - open questions for further research.

3. Depending on availability, we recommend convening an interdisciplinary group from your extended team of partners, adopters, and scalers, particularly frontline end users and key experts.
4. Set expectations: it's still early in the process. Your participants may not see anything that is revelatory to them.

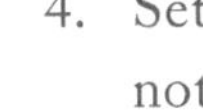

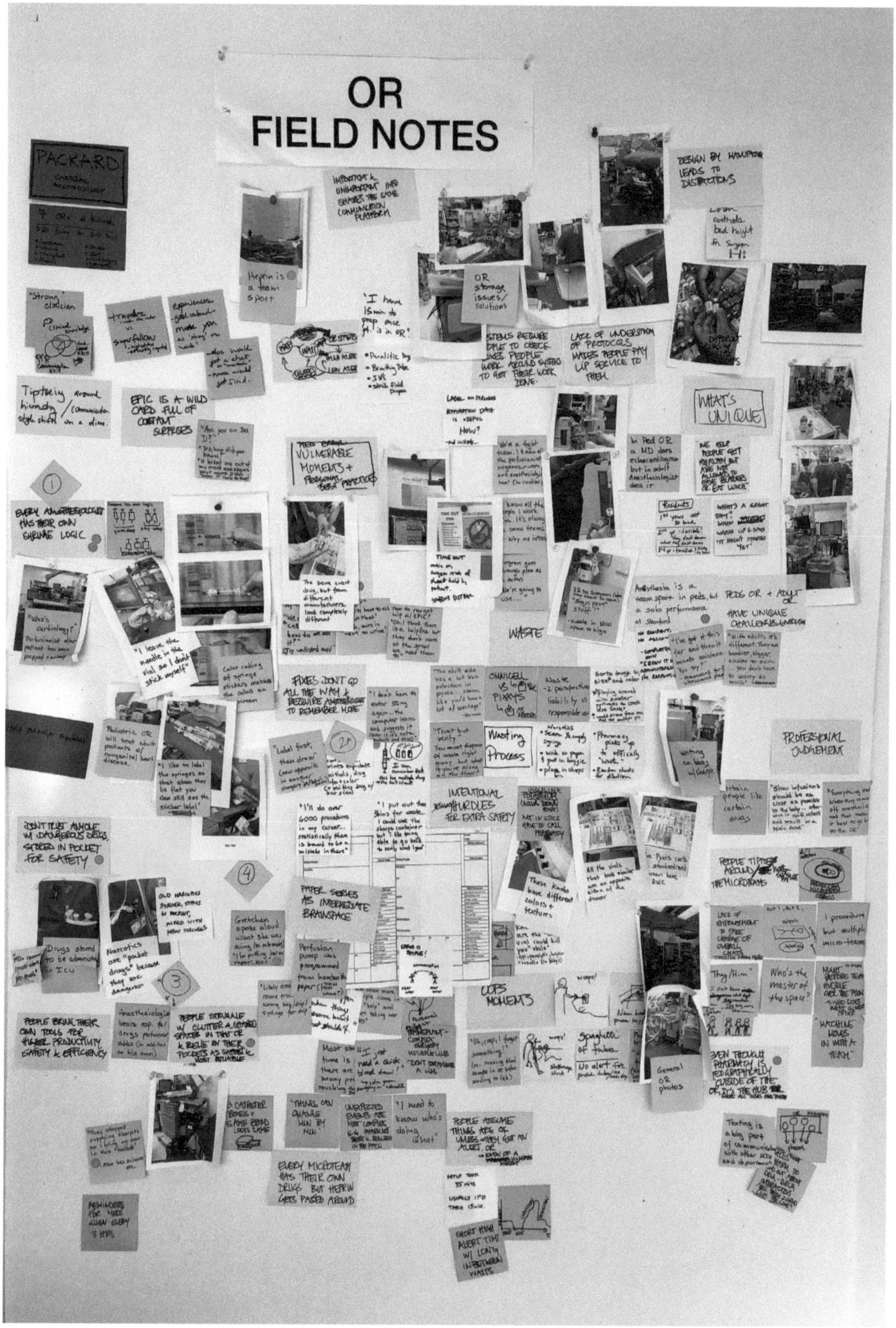

This board contains dozens of observations, quotes, and images from just two visits to the operating room. At the fieldwork snapshot meeting, such as the one on the opposite page, we started with telling stories about who we interviewed and observed, and shared preliminary insights about key dynamics and unmet needs we identified that were creating difficulties and risks in the clinical environment. We shared these emerging themes and opportunity areas and then brought forward questions to stoke discussion with the stakeholder group.

5. Explain the journey to this point, and walk through your boards. Stay in the "reporting" mode; don't try to present anything that delves too deep into the realm of interpretation. This is because you can be sure of what you saw, but you can't yet be sure of what you've learned. Be realistic: you are only a little ways into understanding the challenge with a steep learning curve. Your primary goal is to learn more about what you have learned, not to solve or precisely define any problems.
6. After explaining each board, ask participants to use sticky dots to vote on the themes and insights that feel most important to the design challenge.
7. Gain their feedback about how resonant or important the learning is, where hidden risks might be, and where there may be gaps in your research, understanding, and knowledge. Be open to suggestions that you've missed a piece of the puzzle or may have not dug deeply enough, but beware of scope creep. The idea of design research is not to be comprehensive, but to gain sufficient inspiration to design meaningful and impactful solutions.

By this point in the Discovery Design process you have captured a body of information and begun to extract meaningful insights from them. Let's enter the Synthesize phase.

Synthesize

"Observation reveals what is happening, but it takes interpretation and speculation to understand why."
—Jane Fulton-Suri

Having laid the groundwork for your project, you are ready to weave together the strands of your research and translate them into insights that inspire action. We refer to this process as synthesis. It draws from a rich tradition of social science and design methodologies in order to identify themes from your research, discover hidden meaning, and define new directions for design. Relying in equal measure upon intuition and analysis, the act of synthesis helps us to make sense out of the underlying motivations that animate people's behavior.

The goal of this phase of the Discovery Design process is a sharp definition of insights and opportunities that will help you decide what is important, why it is important, and to identify the real problem. You will then be ready to generate a wealth of ideas about how to solve it.

Process steps

Step 4-1 The synthesis kickoff

Gather your assets and prepare to engage.

Step 4-2 Look for themes

Cluster observations into groups that make sense.

Step 4-3 Create frameworks

Build a conceptual model.

Step 4-4 Generate insights

Turn themes into insightful statements.

Step 4-5 Define opportunities for design

Create design challenges in the form of "How might we…?" statements.

Step 4-6 Synthesis review

Test your assumptions.

Step 4-1 The synthesis kickoff

Gather your assets and prepare to engage

In a 12-week project we advise allocating at least one week for synthesis. During this period you will be reviewing your research findings and generating insights and opportunities. It takes patience, and there may be times when you feel lost in the fog of data. But gradually your way forward will emerge.

Story

"The first time I went through a synthesis process I couldn't get over the fact that we were relying on purely anecdotal stories. The designers made it sound 'so easy to follow your intuition,' but my intuition was to question stories and seek statistically significant data sets. Like many of us, I was schooled in deductive reasoning, and it took me a while to become comfortable with intuitive inferences and subjective judgements. But these insights tell us 'the why' and give us clues as to what to do about it."
— Hospital executive in Northern California

The best way to kick start the process is to schedule a synthesis workshop. This is an opportunity for the core team to review the data it has collected and generate tentative first directions. Three hours usually does it, though large and complex projects may need a day or two. It's worth the investment. Surrounding your core team with the rich body of observations and evidence it has collected is an important step in ensuring team alignment. Keep in mind that one way that qualitative work can be more rigorous is if you have different disciplines engaged in the interpretation and synthesis work.

The goals of a synthesis workshop are to:

- ensure all members of the team have a baseline understanding of what was seen during the research
- share key insights that might have arisen during primary and possible secondary research
- present thoughts and hypotheses that emerged during storytelling.

During the synthesis workshop you will build on the empathy maps and point-of-view statements you developed in the Discovery phase. Here, we look at our learning as a whole and begin to generate possible interpretations. Think of it as the point where your research begins to shift toward more lasting insights and applications.

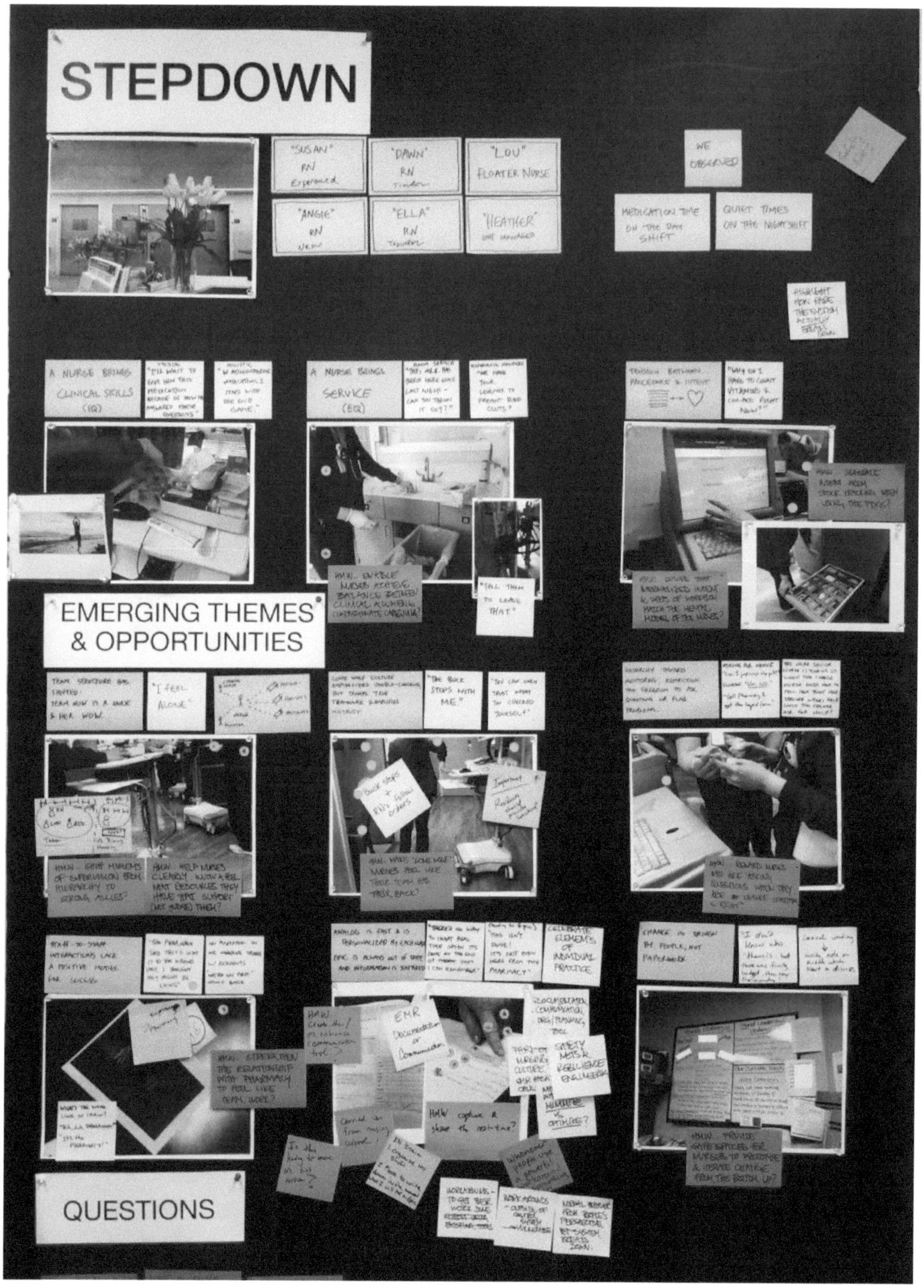

This image shows a synthesis presentation board we used for presenting our ideas to a diverse team of end users. The top section contains learning from observations, interviews, and analagous inspiration, cumulating in three key insights. The next section contains the team's synthesis of potential design opportunities and directions for further exploration. In the final section the team captured questions to stimulate discussion with the presentation participants.

Step 4-2 Look for themes

Cluster observations into groups that make sense.

Sit down with your team and debrief the findings from the fieldwork snapshot. Capture individual observations, quotes, and stories on sticky notes and post them in clusters around the room or on foam core boards. As you do so, rearrange them into clusters as you begin to identify recurrent themes, patterns, and relationships. Watch for puzzling questions, interesting tensions, curious anomalies, and creative workarounds. These are the micro-details that will lead you to macro-insights.

Identify themes

Themes may appear immediately; sometimes they take some time to emerge. Use this workflow as a guide:

1. Find the gold

Give each member of the team 3-5 minutes to recount the most important stories and observations to the team, while the others capture them on sticky notes and affix them to one of your boards. You might find it useful to use different colored notes corresponding to specific groups, quotes/observations, insights, and opportunity areas. To guide team members in the storytelling, ask them to recall the observations that felt most interesting or promising. Use the filter, "is this new news?"

2. Cluster

On a fresh board, bring over the most important sticky notes and cluster them into themes. Trust your team to determine what should be left behind. Did certain issues or behaviors keep coming up? Did different people identify the same pain point? We often see teams stop here and call it done. Keep going.

3. Add evidence

Review what you've got and find additional notes, photos, or quotes that provide supporting evidence for these emerging themes.

4. Refine

Refine the clusters. It often helps to color code them.

5. Name themes

Create headers in which you name each theme, e.g. TRUST, COMMUNICATION, OBSTACLES, etc. These titles describe themes that emerge in your findings, but they are not yet insights. You are looking to synthesize to a more abstract, meaningful level.

Step 4-3 Create frameworks

Build a conceptual model.

A framework is a representation of a system and a way to highlight key processes, tensions, and flows. It is a valuable activity to conduct as you identify themes in your research data. A framework can be expressed as a simple diagram that illustrates the connections among concepts. Visualizing various tensions can reveal clear opportunities for improvement and innovation.

The purpose of frameworking is to characterize relationships among concepts, people, and themes. Frameworks help crystalize our understanding and generate sharper insights. They are particularly powerful for explaining the themes and dynamics you have uncovered that lead to the design challenge you have chosen. An infinite number of frameworks could be created around any challenge, and your task is to find the one or two that best illustrate the theme of your project. We have found the following to be particularly effective.

Journey maps

Journey maps are ways of representing experiences over time. They are powerful tools for describing the current situation, identifying problems or gaps, and revealing design opportunities. Focus on the moments that matter and acknowledge that not everyone goes through all moments. What are key phases? How do people feel at each stage, and what are the needs associated with it?

Add "swim lanes" to help you distinguish among the parallel experiences of multiple stakeholder groups, such as patients, families, nurses, pharmacy, prescribing physicians, and lab technicians. What does a patient's journey look like? A nurse's? A pharmacist's? Many journeys are possible, so think about each one and how it is unique and how it relates to others.

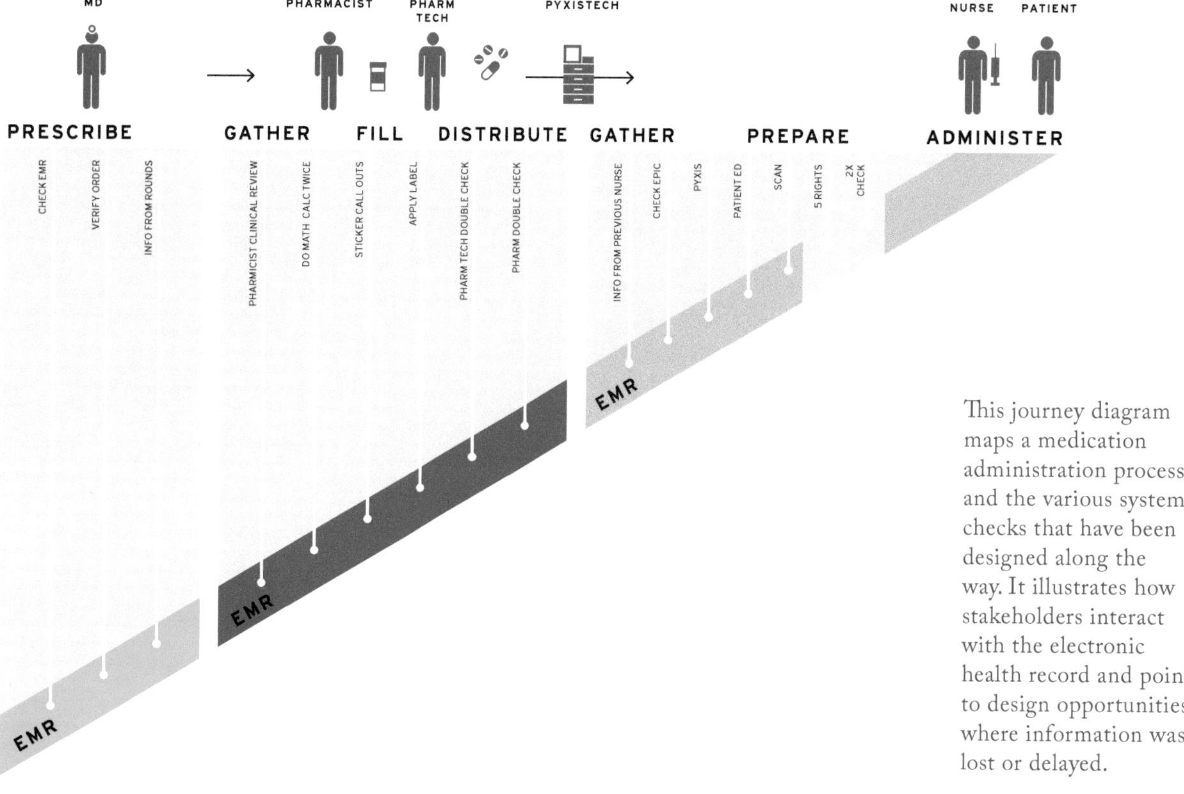

This journey diagram maps a medication administration process, and the various system checks that have been designed along the way. It illustrates how stakeholders interact with the electronic health record and points to design opportunities where information was lost or delayed.

2x2s

A 2x2 can reveal tensions and help categorize contexts or modes of behavior and is a well-tested technique for identifying or evaluating areas of opportunity. To create a 2x2, identify two tensions, dimensions, or axes that are independent of each other. By bringing seemingly unrelated attitudes or behaviors together in the same matrix and allowing for their migration over time, you may make some surprising and unexpected discoveries.

On a project for independent aging, we discovered that not every older adult needed the service we were developing. To align our stakeholders and develop a sharp focus we mapped out behaviors and needs. We arrived at the following segmentation: "High vs low planning ability" (x-axis) and "high vs. low need" (y-axis). We populated each quadrant with the people, relationships, services, and behaviors we encountered in our research. It became clear that the best audience for our new service offering were the people with high needs and low planning abilities.

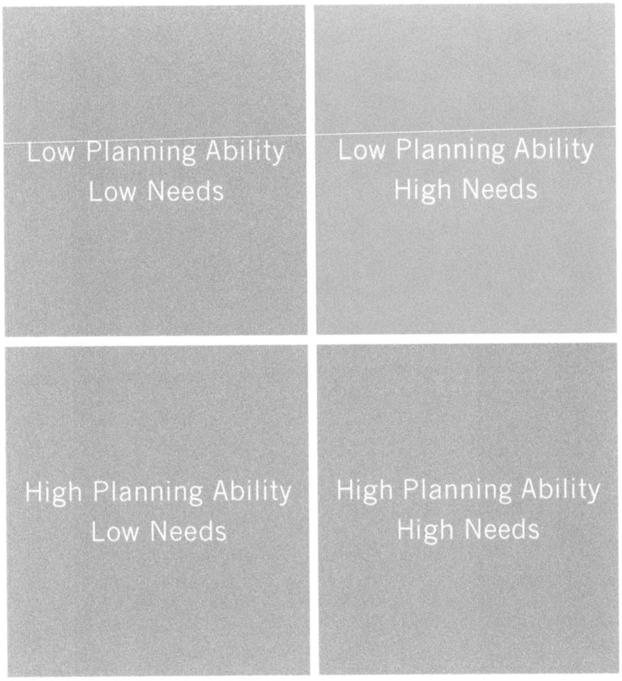

Low Planning Ability Low Needs	Low Planning Ability High Needs
High Planning Ability Low Needs	High Planning Ability High Needs

The following 2x2 helped us map the opportunity space in an open innovation project on medication safety. We observed a wide range of safety practices across the health system, including spaces that had been standardized and those that were completely open to interpretation. The 2x2 helped us compare tools and practices that had been standardized vs. left up to the discretion of the user (x-axis) and those which existed in a shared "we" space versus a private "me" space (y-axis).

Those that fell in the upper left quadrant involved many high-risk spaces where standardization was appropriate: to keep people safe, desired behavior was codified and done the same by everyone. Those in the lower right were spaces where people were free to execute a task in their way, but the zone was low risk, only impacting them. However, we found many areas in the upper right quadrant, where there was high risk created from wide variation in practice in interactive spaces. Practices here suggested opportunities for design.

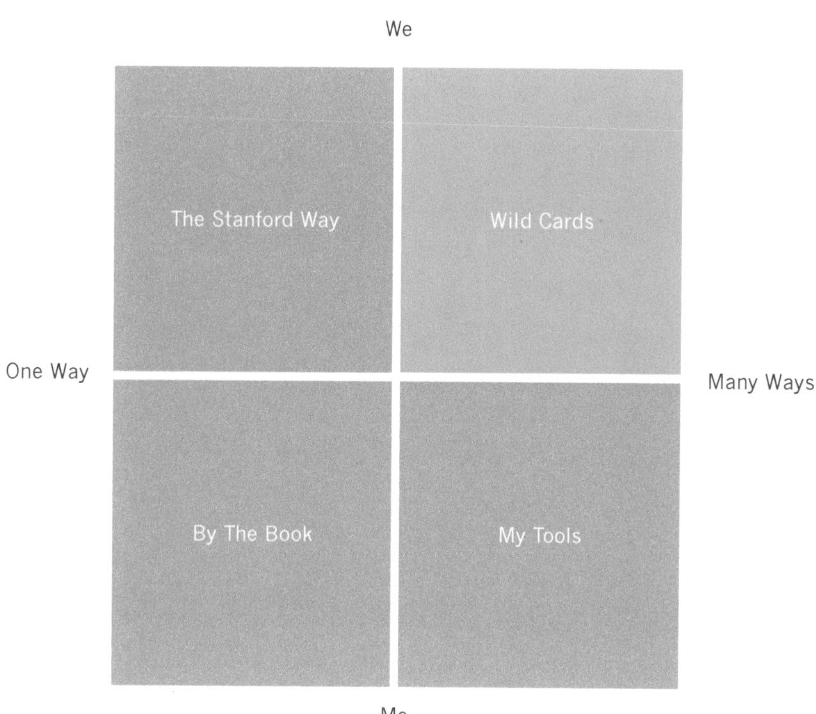

Relationship diagrams

It is often helpful to visualize the dynamics among key stakeholders in a system. Relationship diagrams can help to highlight key themes, visualize the relationships among them, and reveal where patterns might lie.

The following images show the evolution of a relationship diagram that describes information and power flow between prescribers, dispensers, administrators, and patients in the context of medication. Each space between stakeholders points towards a unique opportunity area.

The initial sketch.

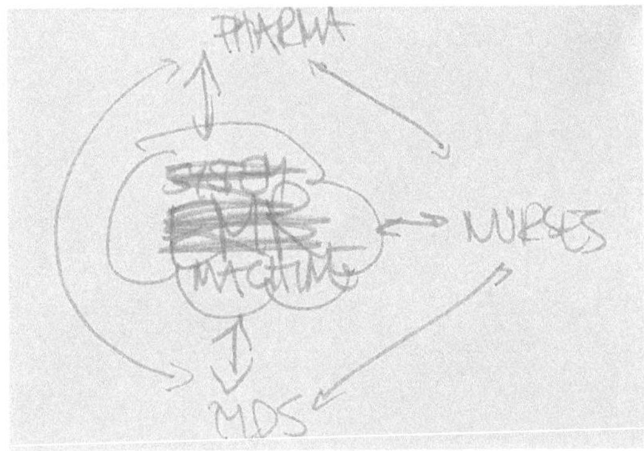

Iterate and iterate.

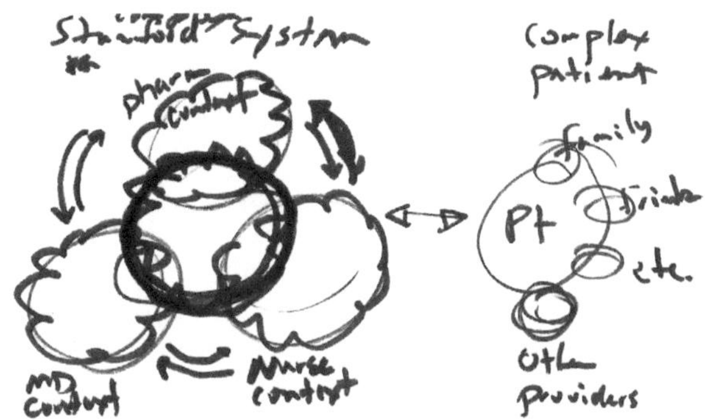

Refining.

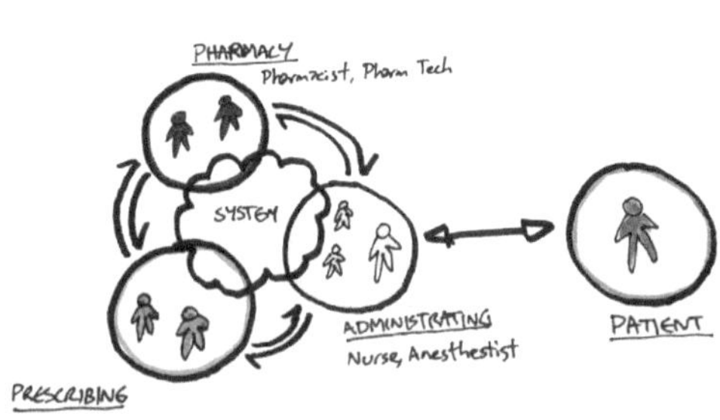

The final product.

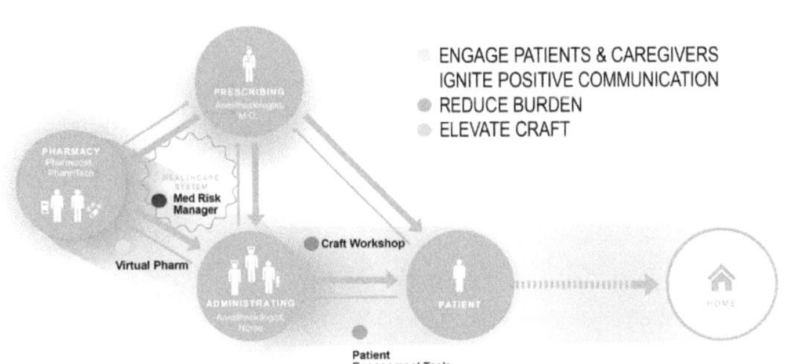

Our team was able to use the relationship diagram to describe some of the information-flow hierarchies we uncovered during our research with patients, nurses, and pharmacists. By overlaying insight statements on top of the framework, we were able to elicit feedback from end users about which ones were most important and where we might have missed something. This was a powerful way of uncovering opportunity areas and provided a launching pad for brainstorming.

Build frameworks

Whichever of these frameworking tools you choose to use, there are a number of techniques that will make them more effective.

1. Draw

Select something that interests you from your research and draw a simple line diagram that explains what you thought was important. Consider moments when the topic seemed to fit into a larger system, or was related or in tension with something else. Add in people's emotions and behaviors. Leave what's boring and obvious; dig deeper when it gets interesting. Follow your informed intuition. Explain it to someone else. If they understand and are excited about it, keep it; if not, discard it and keep going.

2. Reframe

Eventually, you should have at least 10 framework sketches. Perhaps they can be merged. Perhaps one makes several others redundant. Try new ways of drawing them, even if you like the one that you have. Multiple drawings will help you figure out which parts of the idea contain a simple truth.

3. Refine

It's tempting to try to capture everything that you have learned in a single graphic. Resist this temptation! If it can't be explained quickly, it's not a good communication tool. Many of the best frameworks are as simple as a triangle or two overlapping circles. Some design challenges benefit from two frameworks to bring multiple points across.

It's great to layer in more information to your framework, but don't add information that complicates or detracts from the main story that you are telling. We are not mapping out a complete system; rather, we just want to communicate the most important point in a visual way.

Frameworking tools are useful, but can be difficult to master. Set aside enough time to do it well, be patient and persistent, and remember that "the map is not the territory." These are useful ways of representing experiences, not experiences themselves. A good framework helps align stakeholders outside the Project Team and can serve as a shorthand to communicate your insights and reveal opportunities to stakeholders.

For example, the picture below shows a synthesis workshop in which we brought patients, pharmacists, and nurses together and used the relationship diagram described above to gather their feedback and insights as to pain points and opportunity areas.

Step 4-4 Generate insights

Turn themes into insight statements.

Some themes might result in multiple insights, some in one, and some simply dissolve. That's the natural process of synthesis.

Turn themes into insights

"Synthesis methods are the ways in which ethnographic insights lead to new, innovative, appropriate, or compelling ideas… The goal is to find relationships or themes in the research data, and to uncover hidden meaning in the behavior that is observed and that is applicable to the design task at hand."

—Jon Kolko

An insight is a statement of understanding: It identifies a cause and effect within the bounds of a specific context. Additionally, an insight reframes or explains a series of observations or learnings. Elements that seemed not to be part of a story may be explained by an insight. In the context of design, an insight statement is an assertion about people's behaviors, values, and perhaps their underlying mental models that suggest areas to be improved. They may be challenging, counterintuitive, and even disturbing, but each insight points to a potentially positive intervention. Don't be too hasty in accepting or rejecting them. You will have plenty of time to test them later.

Insight statements should be short and catchy and reveal the reason underlying the observation on which it is based. Some are based on explicit needs. When people say, for example, "I need the big corner office [because I have a lot of stuff]." Others point to implicit or unspoken desires, often driven by emotions: "I need the big corner office [because I want to feel important]." An insight statement is something you believe to be true but was derived from, rather than based on, a direct observation. An insight holds for more than one situation. An insight summarizes the stories you heard and often highlights a tension or a shift.

Here is a strategy for translating themes into insights:

1. Review the themes and frameworks you have developed.
2. Think about what the themes and frameworks reveal. Write down as many insights as you can, and don't expect each to be a "eureka" moment. Even something seemingly obvious ("Nurses are more likely to make an error toward the end of their shift.") may trigger someone else to agree, disagree, or build. Aim for quantity vs. quality.

3. Once you have developed upward of 20+ insights on any one topic, refine and select the most important. We like to apply various tests to help us decide whether an insight really matters:

   Where's the new news? Is it fresh and surprising? If it's not new, is it explaining a known fact in a powerful way?

   So what? Is another great way to challenge your thinking and press you to dig deeper.

   Can we be more bold/edgy? Bold statements are generative because they tend to prompt reaction and conversation. A statement that asserts a strong point of view often gets to the root of a problem more effectively than one that is timid and polite. Compare: "Pharmacy is valued more for dispensary than their expertise," and "Pharmacy is the expert, but gets treated like FedEx." Dial up the boldness; you can always dial it back later.

   Prove it! Is this a standalone insight, or does it get stronger when we combine it with another one?

   Now what? Is there anything else that can be added to build empathy for a stakeholder group?

A fresh pair of eyes

It can be very challenging to keep a clear mind when we've heard the same stories over and over. When that happens, bring in a couple of friendly outsiders and conduct an experiment: "We are here to refine the story we want to tell. What works and what doesn't? What is news to you?" Capture their feedback and try alternative ways of telling your story. Also, note what words you choose and which stories you highlight. Is there another story that wants to emerge and be told than what you have?

Story

A project team studying ways for reducing liability risks had reviewed a wide array of data, including incident reports, quality indicators, cultures of safety, patient satisfaction scores, and clinician engagement surveys. The team interviewed and shadowed senior surgeons, anesthesiologists, nurses, midwives, techs, and even patients, seeking to gain insight into the day-to-day experiences on the front line.

Synthesis revealed significant gaps between the physician and nursing teams and suggested that while both groups were passionate about their craft, there was no mechanism for coordinating them. "It's like we know what to do," said one physician, "and we toss the ball over the fence—but no one is catching it on the other side." This insight led the team to recast the department's challenges as design opportunities: "How might we spark effective collaboration among the care team?" "How might we assure that improvements sustain over time?" "How might we build a program we can be proud of?"

The result was a new touchpoint to create a local improvement team co-chaired by a physician and a nurse. While the solution was inspired by best practices at other institutions, empathy and data-driven insights helped uncover a larger design opportunity with a contextually appropriate change model.

Letting go

Some stories may have strongly resonated with you and your team early on, but as your point of view evolves they might not seem to fit anymore. Let them go! Clear out your boards and keep only what's needed. If one of your team members feels particularly strongly about an insight and has a hard time seeing it go, create a "parking lot" where ideas are preserved for possible exhumation later on.

Filter and reconnect to the design challenge

Some insights may be so powerful that they point toward another opportunity area or design challenge that could be explored in a further project. Set them aside. Others may feel important but are not yet fully formed. If you can't flesh them out and reconnect them to the problem you are trying to solve, archive them for future use or try adding different filters. It's essential to maintain your focus.

Step 4-5 Define opportunities for design

Reframe opportunities in the form of "How might we…?" statements.

The next step in the synthesis phase is to transform your insights into opportunities for design, which will in turn serve as the basis for brainstorming. We do this by taking an insight statement and recasting it into a simple and concise question in the form of, "How might we…?" The goal of a "How might we…?" question is to highlight an opportunity. It is an actionable statement that addresses the needs you uncovered in your interviews and observations and captures the insights you derived from them.

The phrasing, "How might we...?" is deliberate. It is not: "How will we?" or "We should..." It is intended to be open and to point to a variety of different ideas and solutions. A good "How might we...?" statement is neither so broad that it can't gain traction nor so narrow that it contains the solution.

"The greatest challenge to any thinker is stating the problem in a way that will allow a solution."

—Bertrand Russell

Too broad: "How might we design for safety?" This question doesn't give enough direction because it doesn't imply a starting point, establish the context, identify the people involved, or explain why there is a need.

Too narrow: "How might we create a designated spot for the pill crusher for each patient room?" This question is too narrow because it is a solution posed as a question, which limits the directions in which the team can go.

Just right: "How might we help nurses anticipate the tools they need for medication administration at the patient bedside?" This question leaves open many potential directions, describes the stakeholders, and describes their higher level need in terms likely to generate a wealth of ideas.

From insights to opportunities

We follow four steps in turning insights into actionable opportunities:

1. Review your design challenge

Write down your design challenge on a large sheet of paper and post it where it can be seen by everyone.

2. Select insights

Look around you to remember the stories from your interviews and observations. Drawing from the insight statements you have developed, have everyone come up with three to five that feel most important to your design challenge. As a group, choose the five that feel most responsive to your design challenge to take forward.

3. Generate HMWs

Take each insight statement, and come up with five responsive HMWs—brainstorm individually, and then share them as a group.

4. Select

For each insight statement, select the top three HMWs to take forward into brainstorming.

Generating effective HMWs

Creating actionable HMWs can take a little practice. Here are some tips for taking your insights and translating them into design opportunities:

- Amplify the good
  Take something existing from the system and use it to solve a need.
- Remove the bad
  Separate, protect, or shield end users from pain points.
- Explore the opposite
  Reframe a pain point as an opportunity that can be leveraged to solve a need.
- Address experiences
  Transform a negative feeling into a positive one.
- Identify unexpected resources
  Leverage time, money, emotions, and people to fulfill a need.
- Create an analogy
  Generate ideas by thinking how the context could be redesigned into an analogous context, such as a hotel, a theme park, or NASA.
- Change a status quo
  For example, instead of shielding the nurse from distracting patients during medication administration, we could ask, "HMW engage the patient in the process?"
- Break the challenge into pieces
  Address individual users, experiences, stakeholders, and systems separately.

Your Design Challenge

Insight

HMWs: 1)
2)
3)

Insight:

HMWs: 1)
2)
3)

Insight

HMWs: 1)
2)
3)

Insight

HMWs: 1)
2)
3)

Here are some examples of the full cycle of translating Observations into Insights and Insights into Opportunities. The first two are from a project focused on medication safety. The third and fourth come from a design project to turn the daily nebulizer struggle into nurturing moments for a parent and child.

Example one

Observations and quotes

"My first thought was, 'That's a lot of pills,' but I didn't want to sound dumb." —Nurse

"The pharmacist said it was delivered, but I think he was lying." —Nurse

"It's important to know the nurse so that when she shows up hysterical you can know if she's over-reacting or not." —Pharmacist

Insight

Communication is the foundation of safety, not a luxury.

Opportunities

Go wider than your stories: "HMW forge strong relationships between pharmacists and nurses?"

Align people's interests: "HMW create shared safety mindsets between pharmacy and nursing?"

Highlight needs for communication: "HMW bring transparency to the needs of nurses and pharmacy?"

Include the journey: "HMW bring the unique expertise of the pharmacist to the bedside?"

Learn from each other: "HMW provide positive feedback when collaboration is working well?"

Tip

Below are some suggestions for framing powerful opportunity statements, or HMWs. You'll see how these have been incorporated into the examples provided here.

- Go wider than your stories.
- Include other stakeholders.
- Align people's interests.
- Highlight needs for communication.
- Include the journey.
- Learn from each other.

Example two

Observations and quotes

"As the nurse, you are the face of the system. There is clinical judgment of course, cleaning up… let's call it hospitality, care coordination (such as, calling up physical therapies)... and there is babysitting. Playing with the babies is the best part of my job."

"The orthopedic team just shows up and expects to be prioritized."

The pill crusher isn't in its usual spot, so the nurse has to leave the patient's bedside to find it. On the way out, her input is solicited by her superior for another initiative.

Insight

Nurses must always be "on," despite interruptions

Opportunities

Go wider than your stories: "HMW help nurses show up for medication administration with everything they need (medications, crushers, supplies, apple sauce etc.)?"

Include other stakeholders: "HMW elevate the moment of medication administration to patients, families and other providers in meaningful ways?"

Align people's interests: "HMW involve families and patients during medication administration and leverage their interest in safety?"

Highlight needs for communication: "HMW help clinicians to signal to others when they are not available for non-clinical tasks?"

Learn from each other: "HMW share people's creative solutions among teams and across different units?"

Example three

Observations and quotes

"He complains and asks: Why me? Why do I have to do this? It's hard on him, especially when he sees his brother running around and playing." —Mother

Child kicks and screams and doesn't want to use the nebulizer. After some bribing with a cookie, mom gets her daughter to sit down. The girl endures the treatment.

Insight

Child resistance is a family affair.

Opportunities

Think of the entire journey: "HMW engage the child from the beginning to the end of the nebulizer treatment?"

Highlight the opposite: "HMW include other family members in a shared experience?"

Example four

Observations

"He kept pushing back the mask… wouldn't let us put it on. We still hold the mask, and he still pushes back"—Mother of a 4-year-old boy.

"I also don't like this (nebulizer) device. It looks like I'm gassing my child."

Insight

Parents feel guilty for "torturing" their child with the nebulizer, but do it to provide good care.

Opportunities

Focus on the relationship between people and device: "HMW build a positive relationship between the nebulizer mask and the child?"

Focus on the people around the treatment: "HMW create positive family dynamics around the nebulizer treatment?"

Evaluate your decisions

You should now have reviewed the decision chain to make sure that your team is on the right track and ready to transition from inspiration to ideation.

1. Frame

   Expect the framing of the design challenge to flex as your understanding of the stakeholders, problems, and opportunities has grown. But keep the end in mind: What is the situation you are trying to impact?

2. Alternatives

   Have you gathered enough inspiration pertinent to the design challenge? Have you explored enough of the space to gain a solid understanding of the problems and opportunities?

3. Information

   Is the quality of the data you have collected meaningful and likely to lead to impactful solutions? Has it been validated and accepted as true?

4. Values and preferences

   Have you understood the various stakeholders within the system, and are you able to appreciate what outcomes they care about, what is important to them, and what solutions may or may not work?

5. Logical reasoning

   Do the opportunities for design that you have identified follow from your research?

6. Commitment to action

   Is there sufficient buy in to proceed to idea generation, prototyping, and implementation?

Do a spot check to see where you are, and create action items to address issues where you feel you are lacking. Remember, a decision is only as good as its weakest link!

Step 4-6 Synthesis review

Test your assumptions.

By this time, you'll have generated a wealth of material: 10-12 insight statements, which in turn will have generated several "How might we…?" questions.

You have done the job well when you feel confident explaining it to the people who are closest to the problem, "This is what we have discovered, and this is why it is useful." You will be able to back up your understanding with stories, facts, and observations, and to share this with the people who really live it every day.

Once you are satisfied, it's time to include your stakeholders: show them your insights and HMWs and receive their feedback. Does it resonate with them? What nuances did you miss and they can help you include? Test your findings against their expertise. Expect to hear disagreement and be prepared to learn things that you wish you'd known before. This process builds bridges for implementation.

Even if your ideas are tentative and not fully formed, you will have captured the nature of the problem in a fresh and generative new light. The other half is refinement, and the people in the synthesis review will help you get there.

Your team will have likely uncovered truths that may feel surprising, embarrassing, or confronting to some stakeholders. Therefore, be prepared to meet some resistance and frame your observations carefully.

Furthermore, be ready to respond if stories and observations you present are dismissed by some stakeholders as anecdotal, singular, or otherwise not representative. Design synthesis is the art of sense making where end-user validation is the strongest indicator of front-line reality. However, this is not the full picture. We always want to complement learning from primary sources with insights from leaders, researchers, and related experts. Therefore, ensure that you demonstrate how your synthesis results from the integration of complementary sources of inspiration.

Whom to invite and why

For a synthesis review to be successful, you will need to include people from four groups:

1. Leaders and Decision Makers

    These are the people who sponsor and approve this work, as well as follow on assignments. If one of your opportunities involves IT but your effort is being sponsored through risk management, bring IT decision makers into the conversation as early as possible—both for their buy-in as well as their expertise. Do not hesitate to invite those who might be critical of what you are doing; it is better to invite them early!

2. Frontline staff and anybody else impacted directly

    This is an opportunity to ensure that what you have heard resonates with the audiences for whom you are designing. They are the ones who will let you know what you have missed and if you have misinterpreted a key nuance. They are also the most likely people to credibly confirm your findings while leadership may be disconnected from hard realities. Managers bring their own perspectives, but don't replace front-line staff. Try to get a representative from each group, such as nurses, pharmacy, family advisory council, etc.

3. Managers

    Managers have seen more over-time and can highlight aspects of the problem that might not have come up in conversation, such as technical details, authority structures, or institutional history.

4. Experts

    Especially in academic institutions there are individuals and institutes with particular expertise. Invite them. If leadership isn't available, a representative will be enough to let these centers know what this effort is about and will serve as a connection point for later consultations.

All at once or multiple meetings?

You will need to decide which stakeholders will complement one another and give you the feedback you are looking for. Some areas may prove sensitive, in which case consider hosting multiple reviews with different audiences. Make sure your guests are adequately prepared, and don't let your review session become a battleground for contending interests.

How many people?

In general, a group of 12-16 people will provide you with a broad and diverse range of input.

Difficulty deciding? Here's a tip:

Write each stakeholder group on a 3x5 sticky note ("nurses," "pharmacy," "IT"). Then on 3x3 sticky notes, write names of people and their titles next to the groups: Where are your gaps? Where do you have too many people representing the same perspective? Where are your friends and allies? Who will be challenging, and in which combination are you likely to get the best of their perspectives?

Another tip:

Build strategic allies before the review meeting. Show them the material beforehand and include their feedback. Sometimes you need to be as explicit as to ask an ally to speak up about specific points to back you up.

> "Always design a thing by considering it in its next larger context."
>
> —Eliel Saarinen

Conduct a synthesis review

1. Prepare

To conduct an effective synthesis review, you will need to prepare the ground:

- Create a foam core board for each context you visited—nurses, pharmacy, etc.
- Print out images from your research to support the stories you are sharing, making sure you protect patients and staff identities. Even small thumbnails are helpful to convey a point. Visualize frameworks.
- Provide space for participants to add, adjust, and edit to make them better.
- Post big images around the room of your fieldwork to help keep users' voices front and center.

2. Set expectations

Similar to the fieldwork snapshot at the end of Discover, this is not a moment when you should expect to gain complete consensus. Be sure to explain this at the meeting. A successful review is one in which stakeholders are engaged and help you discover where the gaps are. Reiterate the importance of the project and the costs of doing nothing. Ensure that attendees understand the feedback you are requesting of them and how the meeting will flow.

Story

In a synthesis review, the project team at a large community hospital shared stories from several physicians and nurses about near misses in the operating room that had gone unreported. The team was taken aback when an attending surgeon, who missed the prior meetings, objected strongly: "I'm not sure who you heard that from. We always report near misses." The department chair chimed in: "...and you're right Dr __ , that's how it should be. What we're finding here is that we need to align reporting practice across the department, which could be a big opportunity for safety culture and outcomes. Good work team." With the project co-sponsor's redirection, the surgeon engaged productively in the rest of the meeting and went on to become one of the project's biggest champions.

Moral of the story: Don't be afraid when things get rocky. Make sure you have your co-sponsors engaged and present!

3. Tell stories

Your goal is to draw narrative arcs from what you learned and the collaborative processes by which your insights and "How might we…?" statements emerged. Lead with a story as you share your new view of insights and challenges.

It can be powerful to share how different stakeholders responded to similar questions, revealing divergent assumptions, knowledge, and behaviors. Your voice is authoritative to the extent that it captures the experience of the people you met. The more you can honestly claim that you are simply reporting what you saw and what you were told, the better you will be able to manage any contention.

4. Use specific examples of things that you saw.

Provide imagery to remind people of the things that you saw. Use direct quotes as much as possible, including real, characterful, idiomatic language.

Rather than: "Subjects report difficulty in using the device interface," let them tell their own story in their own words: "One time on the late shift I pressed the 'cancel' instead of the 'pause' button and it never got reset all night."

As an absolute rule, unless you receive explicit permission, do your utmost to protect the identity of the individuals you interviewed or observed.

5. Explain decision criteria

Describe the selection criteria that you will ask your meeting participants to use in helping identify the most meaningful and important insights and opportunities that have emerged from synthesis. We often use the following two questions: "Given the aims of this project…

- which insights feel the most surprising, meaningful, or consequential?"
- which HMWs feel most promising, exciting, or impactful?"

These questions are fundamentally subjective and open to interpretation. They are intended to uncover new learning just as much as to highlight areas for focus.

6. Gather feedback

Provide participants with sticky dots, and ask them to indicate the insights and opportunities that seem most meaningful and important to them. Discuss the results with the group.

Discuss the areas that received the most sticky dots: Why is this insight or HMW so important? Is there something else to be said about this? Are there HMWs we haven't considered?

Review the areas that only received a few votes: Have we missed something important? Are we okay to move on?

7. Be prepared to shift

This is the last moment in the design where you are fully flexible; the intent of this meeting is to lay a foundation upon which all your concepts will be built. It is, therefore, the last chance you will have to test your foundations and give your stakeholders a chance to reinforce them for you. If you are wrong about some aspect (hopefully a matter of nuance rather than fundamental concepts), absorb the new information and adapt accordingly.

8. Explain what's next

Participants might be confused when the meeting ends without a singular HMW to which the project team will direct their focus. Make sure you explain that this is intentional: Convergence will emerge as the team takes the most promising insights and opportunities into the next phases of the project. Explain next steps and when they can expect a progress update.

Reflect

After the Synthesis review, sit down with your team and reflect on what you learned.

Do your insights hold up? Do your ideas still ring true?

Reflect

Are there any new insights or HMWs that have emerged?

Refine your list of HMWs:

How might we...

Next steps

You have chosen your challenge, researched the problem space, and defined clear opportunities for design. This is a considerable accomplishment and of high importance for the overall success of the next phases.

If you feel there are important avenues left to explore, interviews to conduct, or more time required in synthesis, don't shortchange yourself just to advance to the next phase. Discovery Design is about the quality of thinking behind a new product, service or experience, so it's important to feel you've done enough to meet your design challenge. To be sure, there will always be more you could do, and you will continue to gain deeper insights as you move on to testing ideas with users. To help you decide whether you are ready to move on, make use of the decision quality chain we introduced in Step 1-6.

In the remainder of Discovery Design, we will learn how to develop, test, and deploy solutions into the real world:

In **Generate**, we'll learn how to create a large number of ideas for solving the HMW questions we created during synthesis.

During the **Prototype** stage, we'll explore tangible ways to bring ideas to life and test them with our intended subjects. We'll refine the ideas based on what we've learned, and evaluate which solution we think will have the biggest impact using decision science methods.

We'll then shift into the **Pilot** phase, where we'll select the most favored solution and launch it into the real world. In close collaboration with our target audience we'll set baseline measures, track progress, gain feedback, and refine the idea, in preparation for the final phase, **Spread**.

> "If you see a better world, you're morally obligated to create it."
>
> —Genevieve Bell

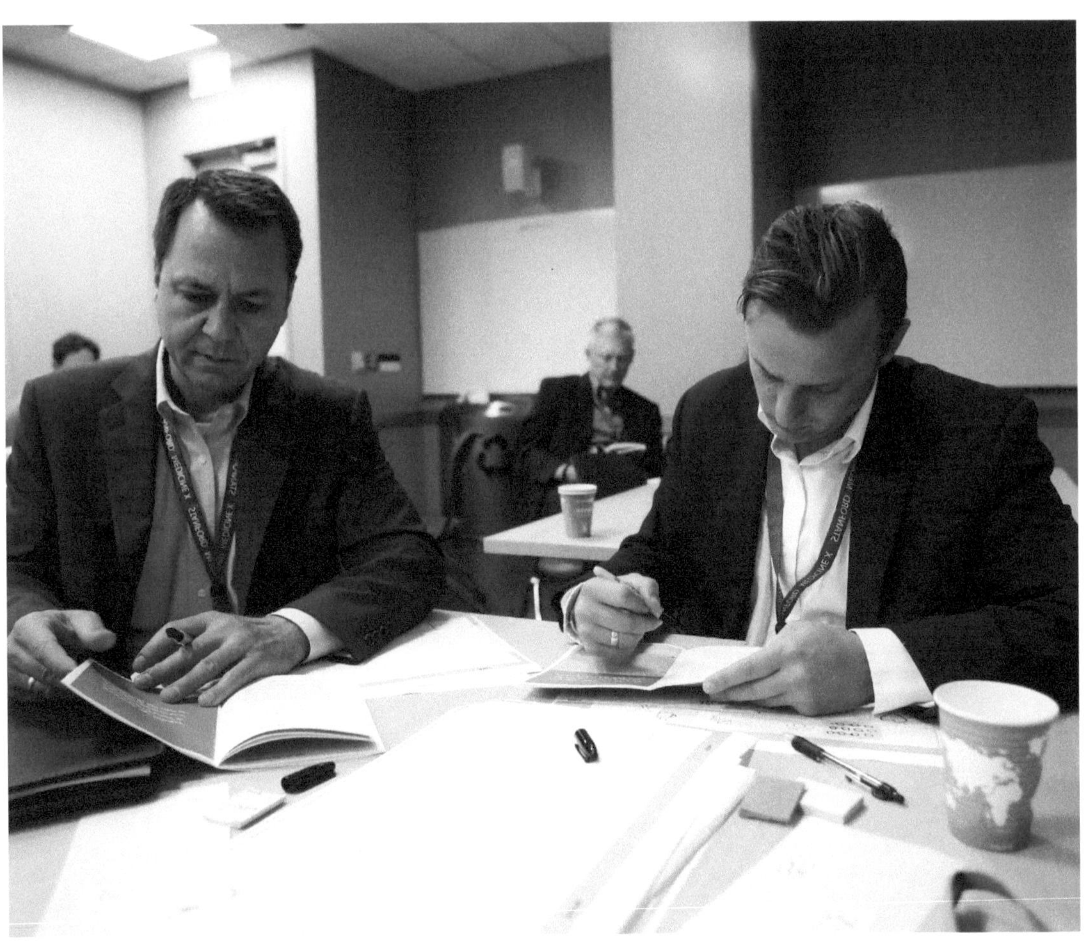

We asked participants in a workshop at Stanford's annual healthcare conference, Medicine X to synthesize learnings and generate design opportunities across a user journey. Once the participants had converged on a problem statement, they then entered a new phase of divergence, generating a large number of ideas to solve their user's need.

Generate

"We want to give ourselves the permission to explore lots of different possibilities so that the right answer can reveal itself."

—Patrice Martin

Once you have explored the territory, synthesized your learning, and fashioned insights into a design challenge, it's time for idea generation. Brainstorming encourages expansive and creative thinking and opens up new avenues to apply evidence-based solutions. From a large set of potential directions, you will engage your intended audience with the most promising concepts. Once you have done so you will be ready to test them with rough and scrappy prototypes.

Process steps

5-1 Brainstorm ideas

Generate a large number of potential solutions and select the most promising.

5-2 Create a concept

Create a concept from the best ideas; show how it might work in the real world.

5-3 Design principles

Identify design principles that emerge from your insights and ideas.

5-4 Research ideas

Collect inspiration that might inform your concepts.

5-5 Refine ideas

Review your concepts and decide whether to carry it forward.

Step 5-1 Brainstorm ideas

Generate a large number of potential solutions and select the most promising.

Brainstorming is a structured group activity intended to generate a large number of ideas in a short amount of time. In this part of the process participants need to feel unconstrained and free to share ideas that might not be expected in the highly regulated world of healthcare systems. During a brainstorming session anything and everything is possible, and a team can explore ideas that in a conventional meeting might be dismissed as impractical or even irresponsible. A brainstorming team is unfettered by the natural tendency to see difficulties rather than opportunities.

Brainstorming rules

Brainstorming has been dismissed as frivolous, unproductive, or at best an amusing diversion—and perhaps with good reason! But practiced in a disciplined, structured fashion, it can be a source of fresh thinking and innovative ideas. In fact, brainstorming needs rules to create a safe environment to take risks, stimulate idea generation, and increase the overall creativity of the group.

IDEO, the prominent Silicon Valley-based design and innovation consultancy, has articulated rules that they have etched on the walls of their meeting rooms to remind participants of the brainstorming etiquette. Having rules visibly posted may help to keep your own brainstorming session focused, effective, and fun. Introduce them at the start of every brainstorm, and if you find the session being derailed, stop, and remind everyone of the rules.

> "The creative adult is the child who survived."
>
> —Ursula LeGuin

Here are the rules that are useful in Discovery Design brainstorming:

1. Defer judgement

You never know where a good idea is going to come from. The key is make everyone feel that they can state an idea without fear that it will be criticized, refuted, or dismissed. That includes your own: Try to quiet the little voice in your head that judges ideas and hesitates to air them until they are fully formed.

2. Encourage wild ideas

Wild ideas often give rise to creative leaps. Confronted with an idea that seems wacky or "out there" we tend to think about what we really want, without the constraints of technology, time, or money. And the next speaker may have an idea about how to reel it back in.

3. Build on the ideas of others

A brainstorming session should not be a free-for-all. Ironically, it is a structured way of breaking out of structures, and this requires some discipline. Rather than leap from one idea to the next, consider how you might carry the last person's idea forward.

4. Stay focused on the topic

Keep the discussion on target and resist the impulse to go off on tangents, tell stories, or be distracted even by interesting detours. Remain fixed on what you're trying to design for.

5. One conversation at a time

Your team is far more likely to build on an idea and make a creative leap if everyone is paying full attention to whoever is sharing a new idea. Side conversations are distracting and undermine brainstorming dynamics.

6. Be visual

Capture each idea on sticky notes and post them in real time. Nothing gets an idea across better or faster. One word may be sufficient; a simple drawing is even better.

7. Go for quantity

Aim for as many new ideas as possible. Crank them out quickly and build on the best ones. Get all the ideas out of your head to make space for new ones. As Linus Pauling observed, "The best way to have a good idea is to have a lot of ideas." And he won two Nobel prizes!

8. Think in systems

Think of ideas that will affect different parts of the system you are working with. What impact could be had on the connections, orbits, partnerships, etc.?

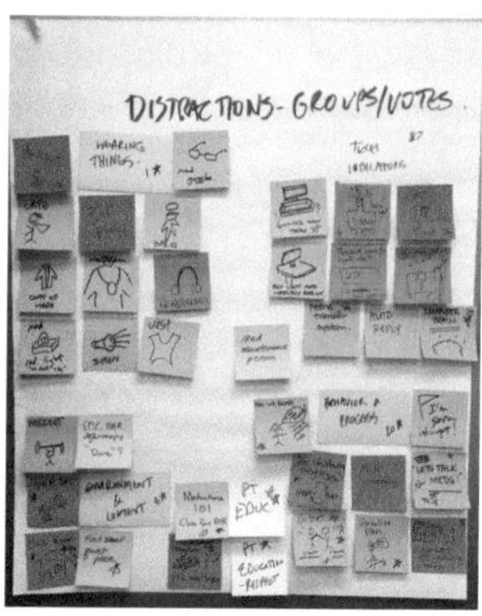

In this brainstorm, pharmacists and nurses came up with many ideas for reducing distractions when dispensing and administering medications. Some were great. Some were crazy. As the group clustered and combined similar ideas, several promising concepts emerged.

"Believing takes practice."

–Madeleine L'Engle

Selecting brainstormers

The success of a brainstorm is dependent on the participants: Select them with care, prepare them well for the mindset they need to bring into the room, and don't be afraid to invite people who know nothing about the project (in fact, they are often best as they are not constrained by what you have seen or heard). It's not easy to create a culture that can support creativity and imagination, but doing so is essential to inspiring a free-flowing exchange of ideas.

Tip

During brainstorming days try to get people out of their day-to-day habits and eliminate the cultural cues of hierarchy. Encourage the team to dress casually; meet in a new space, bring in props, have food, people of diverse disciplines, and don't invite the boss. At the start of the session, the facilitator should prime the creative pump with a few warmup questions: "What if Oprah were to lead the surgical team?" "What would it look like to practice psychotherapy on the moon?" Let the participants know that this is the place to let loose with wild ideas—who knows which of them might contain a practical gem? In our experience, people tend to be self-limiting in sharing of ideas, so the job of the facilitator is to create a safe environment for people to be creative.

Here are some traits to look for:

- Willingness to float untested ideas without fear of embarrassment.
- Ability to speak concisely.
- Appreciation of a process that feels less like a meeting and more like a game.
- A tendency to listen as much as talk.

At the other end of the spectrum, try to avoid the devil's advocate, the old-hand who has "seen it all," the process skeptic who says, "That'll never work," and the alpha male who is certain that "My ideas are best." Don't invite "observers" who will not participate, as they will drain energy from the room.

Each brainstorming session should be focused around a self-contained problem statement that can be set up in a few minutes without an elaborate description of the project.

Finally, include representatives of the population your project is hoping to serve. They will feel like they've been part of the solution and will generate ideas that would never occur to outsiders.

Facilitating a brainstorm

The key to a successful brainstorming session is preparation. To repeat: A brainstorm is not an open-ended free for all; it requires discipline, organization, and preparation.

1. Prepare HMWs

Review your "how might we" questions and select the most valuable that emerged from your Synthesize Review. Each session should include three to five brainstorm questions. A single brainstorm usually dries up after 20 minutes.

2. Time, space, materials, and people

- Set aside discrete time for brainstorming. Aim for 45-90 minutes for total session length. If it's much shorter, you will not have enough time to warm up; much longer and the session will be too mentally tiring and you will see diminishing returns.
- Find a space free from distractions. Ask participants to switch off their cell phones (or leave them in a basket at the door).
- Everyone will need sticky notes and a permanent marker. Prepare some brain food and drinks.
- Select your brainstormers (5 give or take 2 people is a good range) based on the HMW questions you would like to address.

3. Ground rules

Before you begin, the facilitator should explain the rules and tools:

- Have the brainstorming rules written out and displayed prominently in the space.
- Remind the team to use sticky notes and a dark marker to capture

"The early participants dubbed our efforts 'Brainstorm Sessions'; and quite aptly so because, in this case, 'brainstorm' means using the brain to storm a creative problem—and do so in commando fashion, with each stormer attacking the same objective... In this operation all must shoot wild and pile up every possible alternative by way of ideas."

—Alex Osborn, 1948

their ideas—use headlines and a sketch, one per sticky note.

- Explain how the session will work: the facilitator will introduce the HMW for the session. Participants should say each idea aloud to the group so that everyone can hear and build on it. The facilitator can take the sticky notes from people and affix them to the foam-core board so the ideas are clearly visible to the group and can inspire more ideas.

Tip

How to Use Sticky Notes.
Design Thinking is visual. We want to show rather than tell and build a physical, experiential collage of our thinking for making unexpected connections. Working in this way creates a shared understanding of the information, insights, questions and ideas that drive our design work and inspires the way forward. One of the most powerful tools we use are sticky notes, and there is a "right way" for using them!

1. One idea per sticky note.
This helps for clustering similar ideas into themes later.

2. Use headlines.
Use big, bold, clear headlines, not "scribbly" sentences.
This enables everyone to understand and see your contribution!

3. Be visual.
Draw pictures. You may not think you can draw, but you will be surprised at the impact a stick figure, arrows, stars, or other simple images can have for bringing an idea to life.

4. Be a ninja.
Pull your sticky notes off the pad downwards—that way they won't fall off the wall!

4. Warm-up

Lead a five-minute warm up.

The goal here is to break people out of their day-to-day mindsets and get the creative juices flowing. To get everyone comfortable, do an activity such as Crazy-8, a fast sketching exercise that challenges people to sketch 8 ideas in 8 minutes (not 8 variations of one idea or 8 steps of one idea, but 8 distinct ideas). Present a random object from the room, such as a marker, and ask the group to sketch 8 creative uses for it as possible. The more outrageous the better!

Now, run a second, more focused warm up, choose a topic spun off of your HMWs to get people thinking widely and with a sense of possibility. For example, if the brainstorm question is, "HMW improve communication in the operating room environment?", you could prompt the brainstorm with the question: "Come up with as many famous teams as possible!" [Brainstorm] "What makes them so effective?" [Brainstorm]

5. Brainstorm

Announce the HMW to the group and ask everyone to brainstorm on their own for two minutes. In turns, ask everyone to share their ideas and for others to build on those ideas as they do. Let it run until the flow of ideas slows down. Aim for quantity—at least 50 ideas. If a question is not getting traction, leave it and move on. Keep the energy high, and throw in some wild ideas yourself. Remind everyone of the rules, politely but firmly.

6. Spark

The facilitator should be ready to reframe the challenge a few different ways. Think about how to scale the HMW up and down in terms of time, stakeholders, spaces, and resources. For example:

- Space: What if we took over a whole building? What if we only had one room?
- Partners: What organization could you partner with?
- Money: What if it cost $10 million? What if it cost nothing?
- Technology: How will they do it 100 years from now? How did they do it 100 years in the past?
- Mood: What would make it playful? How could we engage all the senses?
- Players: What if it were for only a select few? What if someone doesn't speak English?
- Time: What if we had an hour? Five years?
- Perspective: What would be ideal for your interviewee? What would be ideal for leadership?
- Analogous inspiration: How would (Disney, Starbucks, the Navy SEALs) do it?

7. Vote

Give each person in your group 5-10 sticky dots (approximately 10% of the total number of ideas they are voting on), and after each brainstorm, ask them to vote by affixing a dot to the ideas or clusters of ideas they feel (1) Best meet an important user need, and (2) Have the potential to have a big impact. This "vote" is not a referendum, but a method to identify ideas that are interesting or promising. Vote quickly; go with your head and your heart. Choose the things you are personally most excited about.

Story

A team at a British psychiatric hospital reported on a brainstorming session aimed at reducing the number of assaults experienced by members of the clinical staff: "As the exercise came to an end I glanced around the room at the walls full of flip charts, each in turn hosting tens if not hundreds of 'post-it' notes. And whilst I was delighted with the number of ideas generated, the next task – trying to make sense of them all – had already taken on a somewhat overwhelming quality. With the words "have faith in the process" ringing in my ears, we marched on through the next exercise grouping similar ideas together and starting to build a more coherent picture of the options available to us. By the end of the session one idea—restorative practice—had emerged as the clear favorite amongst the participants. The excitement in the room was palpable. We left with a concept direction and more buy-in than I've ever seen to develop and pilot the solution. A few months on, we've achieved an 50% reduction in employee injuries!"

Select promising ideas

Whereas brainstorming is a group activity, developing an idea usually requires individual reflection or focused dialogue with a partner; the more specific and technical the challenge, the more likely this is to be true. Once the brainstorm is over, the core team focuses on selecting the most promising ideas.

1. Cluster

Review all the ideas and capture any that received votes, as well as any strong favorites that may not. This process isn't about consensus or democracy. If something intrigues you and feels like it's stuck in your mind, save it. There might be something there for the core team to build on. Spatially arrange your ideas to find connections and logical groupings.

2. Find the hidden gems

Your purpose is not to find the best idea, but to identify themes that might live together as a new concept or offering. Sometimes the value of a cluster of ideas isn't the ideas themselves, but a way of thinking about a problem. Although a brainstorm might not generate a solution, it might point to an underlying theme that will.

3. Be critical

The aim of the process so far has been to inspire and inform your intuition in selecting the right ideas, but you have now reached a point where you need to exercise judgment. Not all ideas are created equal; a great idea may not be appropriate in the context of your problem.

"You don't think your way to creative work. You work your way to creative thinking."

—George Nelson

Step 5-2 Create a concept

Create a concept from the best ideas and show how it might work in the real world.

At this point you are ready to begin transitioning from a collection of interesting ideas to a focused suite of concepts that can be refined and pushed forward. Whereas the function of a brainstorming session is to allow your team's thinking to diverge, you will now begin to converge around a single solution to your design challenge.

Create a storyboard

A storyboard is a powerful way to explore an idea and to share it with others. Indeed, you can think of it as your first prototype: Placing an idea in a narrative forces you to think more broadly about the way it impacts others, environments, and how people learn and sustain the idea. Even a very rough storyboard can be helpful when an idea is new and yet to be formed. Sharing it with others is how you will refine it. This is best done by bringing together small groups of people drawn from the population you are trying to affect.

1. Take the most promising ideas that have emerged from your brainstorming. Imagine how these ideas might come together in a real-world concept, and how a member of your intended audience would use, consume, occupy or otherwise interact with the solution you are proposing.

2. Create an end-to-end story, and describe—in words and pictures—what is happening at each moment of the story (using the template on the following page). Use the stick figures we've provided to bring the scenes to life!

3. Think of moments of the whole experience, such as:

- How does a user first encounter it?
- How do users experience it over time? What do they do, and how do they feel?
- What is the most iconic moment?
- How does it impact staff and managers?
- How do you measure impact?
- Who are the other stakeholders in the system that might be impacted?

Patient Joe has had some big changes so the system selects him as one of 6 high-risk patients for the Med Risk Manager (MRM). Risk, ie acuity, # of meds, etc.

MRM starts her shift and sees alert about today's top 6 patients.

Scheduling with nurse. Nurse receives email with option to connect with MRM, can select Y/N/later if she is currently too busy.

RN and MRM meet and have a face to face meeting with the patient. Risk is averted.

MRM PharmD loops MD in remotely. MD adjusts prescription.

In a recent project, we brought nurses and pharmacists together to explore how pharmacy could lend their expertise at the bedside for high-risk patients. After brainstorming many different ideas, the pharmacists and nurses developed a storyboard for an idea for enabling nurses to request a pharmacy consult for patients who were identified as at risk for an adverse drug event via a trigger tool system.

MOMENT 1	MOMENT 2
DESCRIPTION	DESCRIPTION
MOMENT 3	MOMENT 4
DESCRIPTION	DESCRIPTION
MOMENT 5	MOMENT 6
DESCRIPTION	DESCRIPTION

Cheat sheet for drawing people and emotions for storyboards

Joy

Anticipation

Trust

Surprise

Sadness

Fear

In a recent project, we brought nurses together to reimagine the workstation. After brainstorming many different ideas, the nurses created a concept worksheet to develop a perspective on how the solution might operate in the real world.

Reflect

Once your team has sketched a storyboard that communicates their favorite ideas, ask them to reflect upon why they feel strongly about it. Consider gaps in the story, potential challenges, and its potential impact relative to the effort required to implement it.

WHAT MAKES YOU EXCITED ABOUT THIS CONCEPT? WHAT IS UNIQUE AND IMPACTFUL?

WHAT ARE THE CHALLENGES? (CULTURE, WORKFLOW, TECHNICAL)

MARK THE IMPACT OF THIS SOLUTION VS THE EFFORT TO IMPLEMENT IT, AND NOTE WHY:

HOW MIGHT WE TRY THIS IDEA ON A SMALL SCALE/SAFE WAY TO ITERATE?

VERY FIRST STEP 5-TODAY:

NEXT STEP(S) (WHEN:_______)

AFTER THAT (WHEN:________)

Tip

Most professionals haven't tried to draw since they were children; we often hear, "I'm not an artist," to which we reply, "Just try." You'll be surprised how effective storyboards can be in helping you to understand an idea and present it to others.

Tip

At first, new-to-the-world ideas might feel over-ambitious or disruptive. Think about how you might start small with a very first step. What could you execute with $5 and in one day?

Step 5-3 Design principles

Identify design principles that emerge from your insights and ideas.

Design Principles are rules, strategies, directives, or unifying elements that emerge from your creative process. They are the "useful truth" that you have distilled. It may help to think of them as statements of strategy from which specific tactics will be derived.

Design Principles are simple statements that define a requirement of any good solution to your challenge. They can be on any topic: culture, people, processes, or products. They are similar in nature to the 'Insights' that you generated in the previous Synthesize step, but are more specific and actionable. Design Principles are the billboards along the route to a great solution.

Here are some examples of what Design Principles might look like in the context of a healthcare improvement challenge. The more pithy the principles, the more memorable they are likely to be, for example:

> Tools: "Capture and communicate personal preferences."
>
> Culture: "Processes need to be accessible to all shifts."

Well-crafted design principles have the following characteristics:

1. **Empathetic: codify fundamental user needs**
    - based on specific user stories and insights
    - bring user empathy to every product decision
2. **Generative: inspire action**
    - phrased as directives
    - invite creative thinking and concepting
    - highlight opportunities to leverage
3. **Evaluative: enable assessment of the direction**
    - determine which concepts to pursue or drop
    - provide a shared way to measure success

Design principles are not solutions but guideposts relative to which you will evaluate new ideas. They establish direction and set constraints on the solutions you will develop. Design principles should express the values of the stakeholders for whom you are designing. If your solution doesn't take into account their feedback, it may not solve the problem you are seeking to address; indeed, it may not be taken up at all.

For example, if your idea is a communications plan to encourage hand washing among physicians and nurses, neither of whom wishes to be told what to do by the other, a design principle might be: "We must speak in the voice of their peers."

Aim for three to seven principles. They should be formulated in a way that is clear and easy to remember. Too many are too hard to apply; too few will constrain your thinking.

Remember, design principles operate as a group, and it's likely that you'll need to identify several.

Below are examples of design principles that were created for a project at Lucile Packard Children's Hospital at Stanford.

The following principles* emerged from our work, which are guiding the development of the final concepts.

1. Speak in a patient-centered tone

2. Design for a patient room that can be dimly lit

3. Be beautiful when patients aren't actively viewing

4. Command attention, without dominating the room

5. Bring clarity & simplicity

6. Bring a sense of fun to the room

*Design principles are quick, memorable recipes that will help keep further iterations user-centric, consistent with key insights, and mindful of constraints.

Identify design principles

1. Review the themes that you distilled from your design research.

2. Consider the core principles underpinning those themes. Frame these as positive statements that might tell you how and what to design.

3. Are your design principles short and to the point? Do they describe just one idea? If it feels like there are multiple ideas going on, break them into smaller parts.

4. Review your design principles and make sure they cover the key aspects of your solution. Modify any that don't.

5. Be prepared to revise your design principles as you start to build prototypes and test your ideas. Some design principles won't reveal themselves until you've built and tested something, but once you spot them, they'll seem obvious.

Step 5-4 Research ideas

Collect inspiration that might inform your concepts.

Explore what's been done. Before you move on to prototyping your idea, you'll need to review the literature. Innovation does not equal invention, and effective solutions may have been tested in other settings. Conversely, there may be paths that others have followed without success, but that might flourish in a different context. Watch for tools you can borrow, lessons you can learn, and approaches you can adopt. Picasso was not the first to observe that "good artists borrow; great artists steal."

Places to look include:

- **Societies, foundations, and institutes:** see if something similar has been tried anywhere else and what may have been learned already.
- **Journal articles:** peer-reviewed, popular, and professional.
- **Vendors:** there are likely companies who have offerings that may be responsive to your design challenge. Some startups might even be looking for opportunities to support an in-hospital pilot. Might there be opportunities for collaboration?
- **Analogous situations:** How has the problem you've identified been solved in other arenas? For example, what can you learn about the information flow in a museum that you could use to inspire information flow in hospitals?

Be careful to remain faithful to the needs and insights you are addressing and the design principles you have identified. A vendor may have developed a solution that purports to solve your subjects' needs, but has it been designed with them in mind? How would they receive it? Would it work in the context to which it is deployed?

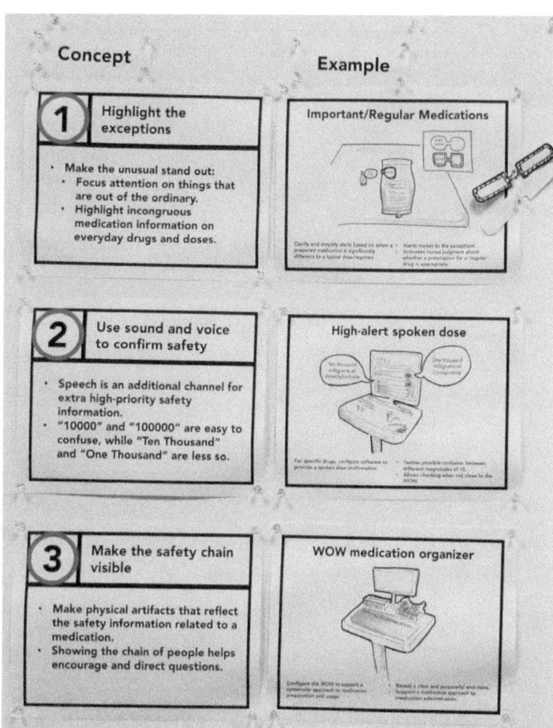

This is an example of a concept presentation board with three concepts for improving medication safety. These were presented to frontline and senior stakeholders who had the opportunity to ask questions, give feedback, and build on the ideas that they felt had potential.

Step 5-5 Refine ideas

Review your concept and decide whether to carry it forward.

Get early input on early concepts. The more feedback you get, and the earlier you get it, the more stable your ideas will be. Early input avoids having good ideas shot down by minor flaws. Conversely, it is wise to let weaker ideas go, making space for other, stronger ones. Just remember that we are evolving ideas, not evaluating them.

Gathering input

Asking for feedback can be difficult. It can also produce a wellspring of inspiration when done well. Here are some tips to guide you:

- **Low resolution:** Let your participants know that the ideas are very early in development. They are intentionally rough, and it will not hurt your feelings if they don't like them. Let them know that their input will help to make your ideas better and that you are ok letting them go. Better now than later!

- **Make it tangible:** Bring visuals (2D drawings, storyboards, or skits) that can be marked up or altered on the fly. Bring extra copies, markers, stickers, and rough prototyping materials.

- **Keep sessions small:** No more than 1-3 people to make sure that all voices are heard.

- **Don't "pitch":** Describe each concept with neutral language. You are looking to understand the nuance of the need just as much any one particular solution.

- **Take time to warm up:** Begin each session getting to know your participant. It is time well spent in gaining rapport as well the context of their input.

- **Practice active listening.** Watch and listen for body language clues: You may notice pauses, small glimmers in their eyes, head tilts, smiles, or hear niceties such as: "Well... that would be a good solution for someone else, but not me." Who is that "other" person?

- **Reflect and re-direct questions:** Refrain from answering questions directly; instead, redirect them. For example if someone asks, "What is that for?," or, "Is that an xyz?," you might respond as follows: "What do you think you could do with it?," or, "What would you like it to be?"

Prepare to share your concept

The next step is to create a concept description for the idea you would like to prototype and test. This is a useful tool for refining your thinking and a means for gaining feedback and buy in.

CONCEPT NAME	WHAT NEED OR OPPORTUNITY DOES THE CONCEPT ADDRESS?
ONE-SENTENCE DESCRIPTION	
HOW DOES IT WORK?	WHAT DOES IT INVOLVE?
SKETCH THE IDEA	WHAT DO YOU HOPE TO LEARN BY PROTOTYPING THE IDEA?

Host a concept review

With a suite of concepts ready, invite your project team, leadership, and partners to a hands-on review session. Be sure to include representatives of your target groups, especially those that were part of your research. Feedback is not only critical to your own process; people who feel that they have participated in the process are more likely to give your pilot a fair hearing.

The Concept Review is an opportunity for you to share your observations, thought process, and initial conclusions, and to receive essential feedback from key stakeholders:

- It will reveal any flaws, cracks, or gaps early on, when it is easiest to address them.
- It will demonstrate your attitude to the people who will use and test your ideas later on.
- It will build momentum for later prototyping.

Here are some steps that will lead to a successful Concept Review:

1. Create a space for each concept to be pinned to foam boards. Each one can be represented by sketches, storyboards, skits, and prototypes.
2. Try a "science fair" approach to concept review: One person from the core team will present each concept. Split the reviewing group into teams of 3-4 people to rotate to view and discuss and build upon each of them. Give each reviewer sticky notes, markers, extra paper for sketching, and prototyping supplies for ease and flexibility in giving input.
3. Rotate through each concept, collecting all input visually, then allow reviewers to place top votes on their favorite concepts.
4. Discuss.

At the end of this meeting you should have a selection of top concepts to refine for building and gathering input from real users.

We conclude this phase with some warnings we have learned from experience. First, beware of the temptation to "sell" your idea. Design is not a process of persuading anybody of anything. Unlike marketing, which has been described as the business of selling the story, designers are in the business of finding the truth.

Second, master the discipline of letting go. It's inevitable that members of your team will have "pet" ideas, and it's natural for individuals to become attached to ideas that they personally crafted. One of the traps that can corrupt your innovation process is picking favorites too early and hanging on to them too long. Console yourself: sometimes an idea that falls by the wayside comes back later on as a small part of something better. As William Faulkner observed about writing, the key is knowing when to "Kill your little darlings."

And now, let's Prototype!

Prototype

"Do not seek praise. Seek criticism."

—Paul Arden

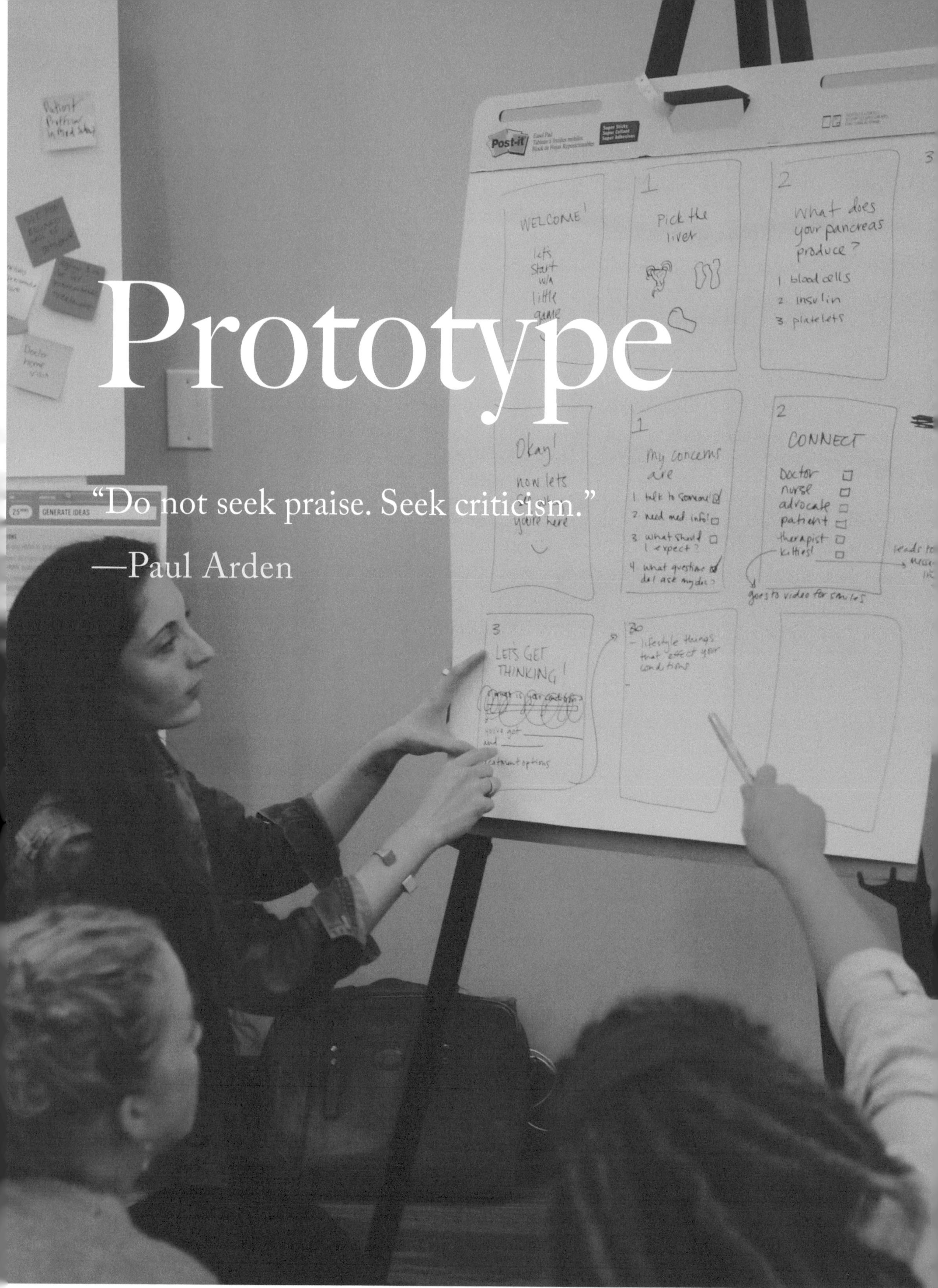

Designers have learned the importance of prototyping as a way to work out the kinks before seeking regulatory approval, manufacturing support, or taking other major steps. Sometimes a strip of duct tape and a bar of soap are enough to give form to an idea to clarify its underlying design principles. It's fast, and cheap, and as a learning tool it can provide maximum return on minimum investment. Once you have tested your idea through a series of rough prototypes, gathered feedback, and made the necessary adjustments and refinements, you will be ready to pilot it in a real-world setting.

Process steps

6-1 Build your prototype

Learn how to prototype a product, a service, an interface, or an environment.

6-2 Capture and integrate feedback

The point of a prototype is to elicit feedback.

6-3 Refine

Iterate and refine until you are satisfied that you're ready to carry your idea forward.

6-4 Share the concept for launch

Bring your idea to life.

Step 6-1 Build your prototype

Learn how to prototype a product, a service, an interface, or an environment.

What is a prototype? A prototype is anything that allows you to express an idea. The goal is not to make a beautiful model, but to gather feedback to see if the idea has value. Prototyping is a critical tool in the Discovery Design process as it lets us test our assumptions through a series of safe, fast, and inexpensive experiments. Unlike scientific experiments that aim for strict, repeatable results, prototypes are more akin to prompts for conversation; they are allowed to change, and we expect them to.

Prototypes start simple and are iterative: They build on what you have learned and become increasingly sophisticated as they address increasingly complex problems. For that reason, it is important to be clear about the question you are trying to answer. A single question could be answered by various prototypes, and iterations can lead to more questions. You'll need to proceed quickly but cautiously. Precisely because it is rough and unfinished, a prototype is vulnerable and can be dismissed too easily. Make sure you have captured what's right about it and not just what's wrong.

Your team should be prepared to create as many prototypes as possible, in each case finding the cheapest and fastest way to test the assumptions underlying an idea. Don't expect to test everything at once; each element will likely go through several rounds of prototyping in varying degrees of resolution as you move from drawings to PowerPoints, process maps, and even physical artifacts. This may sound like a lot of work, but it is an excellent risk mitigation strategy and will save time in the long run. It's also loads of fun!

In the risk-averse world of healthcare, failure implies error, harm, and injury. Discovery Design takes the opposite approach: failure implies learning. We believe that in a complex innovation effort there are always many more ways to fail than to succeed and that the best strategy, in the words of IDEO's David Kelley, is to "fail early to succeed sooner."

> "If you're not prepared to be wrong, you'll never come up with anything original."
>
> —Sir Ken Robinson

Why prototype?

There is a common misconception that a prototype is the first version of the idea that you intend to implement. This type of thinking is risky and wasteful. The more finished the drawing or model, the more difficult it is to let go of it, even in the face of negative feedback. It can lead to an "escalation of commitment" to an untested solution.

Designers prefer to think of prototyping as a series of small, low-cost experiments from which to learn quickly. The point is to test a broad range of ideas as early as possible to dispose of most of them. A new electronic health record interface can be prototyped by affixing sticky notes to the screen of a phone. A new discharge procedure can be prototyped by drawing a rudimentary storyboard or performing a simple skit.

Prototyping can be a fun and immersive experience, so involve as many of your team members as possible. It is an excellent way to build ownership, especially as new team members enter the process. Take them through your early Observation and Insights phases and let them absorb stories and develop a connection to the big picture. Make sure that everyone has frequent opportunities to share their input and ideas and that they do not feel that key decisions have been made prior to their input. Above all, remember that during the Prototype phase we are not just prototyping solutions. We are prototyping ideas to test our assumptions about a solution.

In this chapter, we will explain how to move from an idea to something that can be tested in a clinical setting. We will also learn how to prioritize questions that can be answered by prototyping and how to gather feedback. Remember that a prototype needs only to be "good enough." At this stage of the Discovery Design process, the key is to move quickly to learn as much as possible.

Choose a prototype form with the right level of investment. It should represent the experience you are bringing to life and ask the questions you hope to answer, with minimum time or resources. Think paper and pipe cleaners, stick figures, and sticky notes for your first round of prototypes.

Story
A sports clothing manufacturer wished to sell a smart shirt with integrated sensors. The design team prototyped these shirts by placing painter's tape on various sport shirts and taking them out to athletes. This crude prototype led to a discovery that completely changed the design direction: men loved wearing old race shirts! They had an emotional connection with certain shirts that reminded them of successful races they had participated in. The company responded to this observed behavior by designing a clip for the shirt instead of smart clothing.

Story
Working on a project about a new pharmacy tool, we noticed that pharmacists work at high countertops, and we created a system that would work mounted underneath the counter. Pharmacists hated it! If we had not prototyped this setup and tested it with our intended user group, it might have been implemented as a solution, with disastrous results!

Early prototypes should be intentionally low resolution. At this stage, prototypes represent a concept direction; only gradually will they come to life as a specific idea. Building flexibility and ambiguity into the style of building the prototype helps an idea grow, and allows for the creativity and vision of real users. If it looks too good or too perfect, people will have a harder time giving honest input. Prototypes should be made to be marked up, taken apart, and broken.

This is the moment when a good idea gets transformed into an emotional experience!

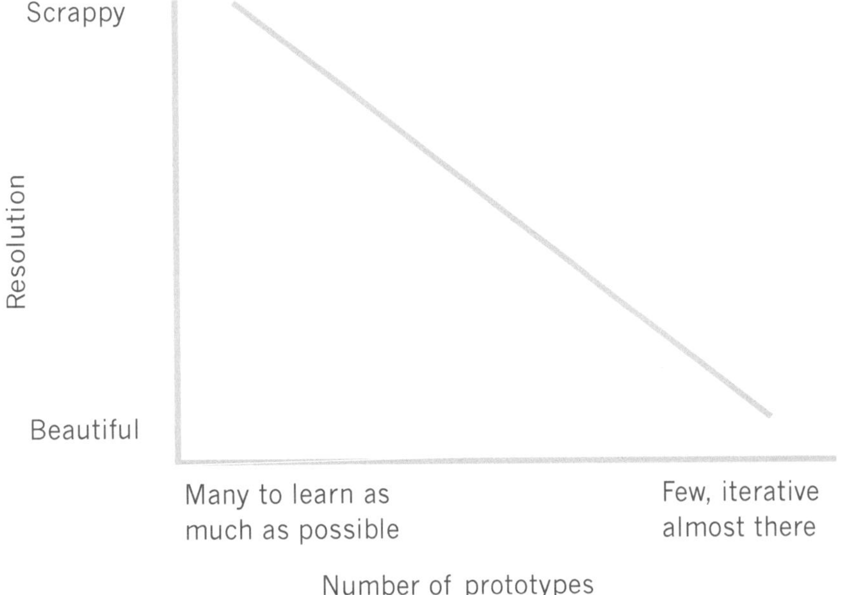

What can be a prototype?

Prototypes can take a variety of forms ranging from storyboards, digital mockups, and role playing to physical artifacts, simulations, or experiences. What all prototypes have in common is that they are in some way tangible and are meant to be shared with other people with the goal of gaining feedback on the concept.

Storyboards

You have already created simple storyboards as part of the Generate phase. A prototype storyboard may be higher resolution and have a greater level of detail—perhaps six or eight panels rather than four. As you learn about the idea, add panels. How does the patient's family interact with the procedure you are proposing? How about the technician who services the medical equipment you want to install?

A storyboard enables users to visualize the experience of your concept as a journey through various moments, and is often the most compelling way to communicate an idea. You don't need to be an artist to create a compelling one. Use sticky notes and don't spend an excessive amount of time. If you have cartoonists on your team, by all means, take advantage of their talents. When it's time for review, consider hiring a contract illustrator to make your storyboards sing. Here, with strikingly different levels of resolution, are examples of storyboard evolution:

1. Sticky note storyboard

2. Concept overview

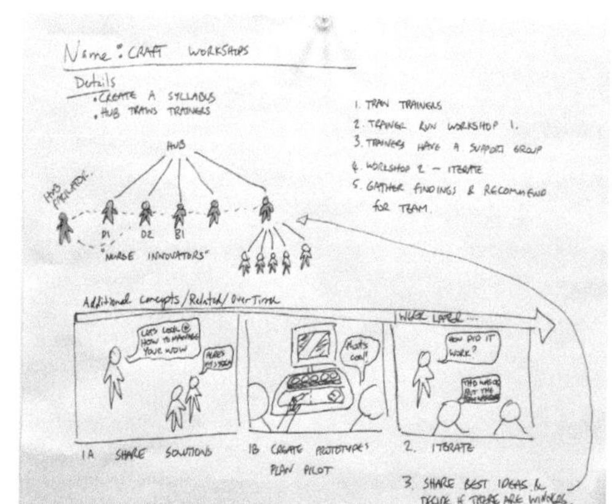

3. Refined storyboard

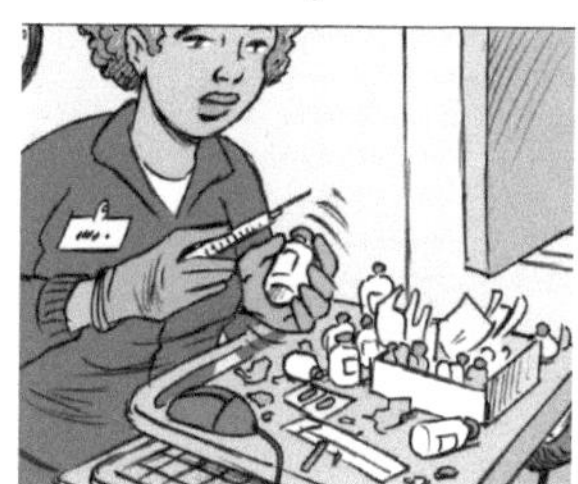

Story

A large multi-site health organization was trying to develop a review process for projects designed to protect patient privacy and prevent duplicate efforts. The team had hit a brick wall—too many stakeholders with strong opinions and a lack of leadership buy-in. Proposing an oversight process wasn't exactly popular. After three years, the team reframed their efforts through the lens of Discovery Design. First, they met with potential users of the new system to understand their needs, concerns, and pain points in dealing with the current system. Then the team brainstormed solutions with different user groups. Finally, they built rough prototypes of new workflows, digital systems, and other workflows. Making ideas tangible broke the stalemate. Hospital leaders understood the value, felt ownership, and came together to co-design a new solution that was rolled out across the whole organization.

Story
In a recent project, the team developed an idea for a video-chat solution for enabling more effective communication from an infusion center and centralized pharmacy. For the alpha pilot, they used a "Wizard of Oz" method of simulating how a digital solution might work by having a pharm tech stationed by the medication dispensing system to answer questions and track where medications were in the system.

Role-playing as a prototype

If your idea involves a new interaction, act out the experience with members of your team taking the key roles. Enacting the interaction will expose gaps in the story and lead you to new questions: "Where does that packaging go once the medication is opened?" "How does the pharmacist learn about a proposed new policy?" Set aside job titles, status, and egos, and don't be afraid to be silly!

When you are ready, take the idea into its intended context and, if possible, involve the people who will actually apply it. You will very quickly learn how this interaction feels and where shortcomings may lie. Remember, you're not just prototyping a thing; you're prototyping an experience.

Software mock-up

If your idea is a new app, digital tool, or website, you can build mock-ups using simple sketches on paper or sticky notes. To simulate a digital experience, paste these onto an actual device or computer; peeling off a note is equivalent to a click. For more complex workflows, lay out paper sketches of screens on a table and invite your subjects to move through them sequentially. Watch for points of hesitation or confusion.

As your ideas evolve, you can use digital tools to help you into higher resolution prototypes; Balsamiq, Marvel and proto.io are just a few of the easy-to-use tools now available. A new process, structure, network or journey can be mapped with sticky notes or by using a program such as Microsoft Visio or MindNode or Mural.ly.

These programs allow you to quickly build smartphone, tablet, and web interfaces with minimal effort. Programs such as Balsamiq are particularly well suited to Discovery Design prototyping as they display an interface as if it were sketched in pencil on the screen using standard interface elements (e.g., "the pull-down menu"). This conveys the 'rough' nature of the prototype and prevents your participants from becoming distracted by choices such as colors or font.

This prototype app, "Me and My Meds," was created using nothing more than PowerPoint. Showing these static images as if they were actual "pages" created a valuable medium-resolution prototype.

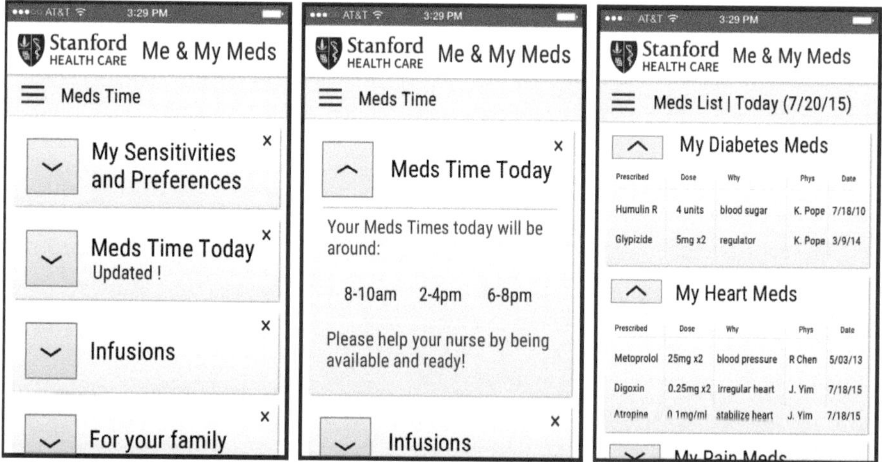

When prototyping a software experience, always use real devices in actual spaces. You don't want to find out last minute that something doesn't work because of a physical limitation or some other unforeseen problem.

Physical model

Create a three-dimensional representation of your idea using cardboard, paper, pipe cleaners, fabric, and whatever else is at hand. "Quick and simple" goes a long way to bringing an experience to life. You may need to exercise caution in using certain materials in a hospital setting, but do not allow this constraint to limit your imagination for prototyping.

Imagine that you are considering a bedside tray that could be used in drug verification. One set of prototypes might focus on size and location; another on attachment methods (magnets, tape, etc.); and yet another on how and when it would be installed. Materials for prototypes of this sort can be found at any local hardware store and modified.

Build your prototype

Review your concept and identify the core elements you want to test with your intended population. If you are thinking about employing an established evidence-based practice or a marketplace solution provided by a vendor, be sure that you are not making assumptions that are inconsistent with the problem you are trying to solve, the context in which it will be applied, and the people who will be affected by it. Think about how you might verify that your assumptions are true.

While still at low resolution, make three different prototype versions of your idea. Photograph your prototypes in context; if this is impractical, you can always resort to Photoshop. In general, the fidelity of your prototype should match the fidelity of your thinking. When you are developing early stage ideas, quick and rough prototypes are appropriate.

Finally, when building a prototype, think "show" instead of "tell." Ask what people see and how they would use the prototype as they understand it. They may ask you for clarification, but don't give in.

Remember, each failure brings us closer to the solution we are aiming for!

Story

A medical device company was working on a new hand-held surgical instrument that included a housing for a bulky gas cylinder. In a single day, using simple materials such as clay, wooden dowels, and metal tubes, they were able to explore a wide range of device architectures. With a member of the team playing the role of the patient (lying on a conference room table), physicians on the advisory team were able to experience how a wide range of different architecture solutions affected their ability to control the device and opened up new conversations about how these choices affected their surgical technique.

The evolution of a concept

We worked with patients, families, and nurses at a children's hospital to imagine, "how might we enable patients and families to partner with nurses in medication safety?"

The process began with nurses and patients brainstorming ideas together:

Nurses and patients then built prototypes to explore different directions:

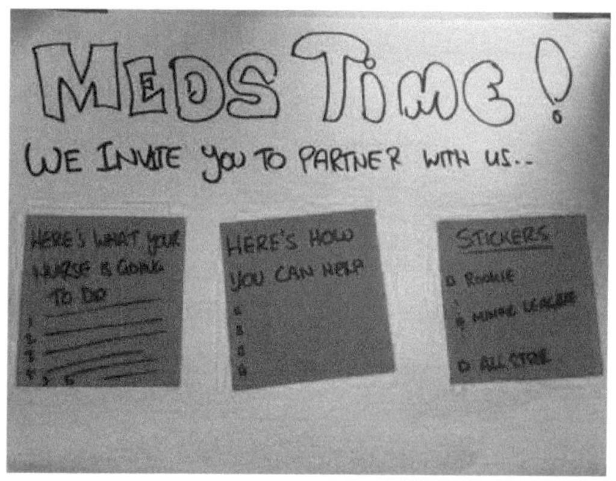

In the lo-fi pilot, nurses tested and iterated the ideas on the unit:

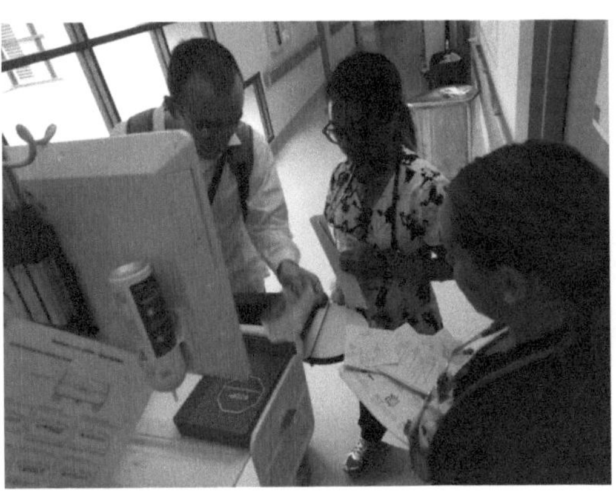

In the later pilots, the team made small refinements, evaluated impact, and received approval to implement the solution organization-wide.

Step 6-2 Capture and integrate feedback

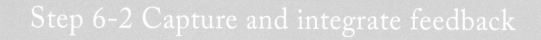

The point of a prototype is to elicit feedback.

Ultimately, the goal of prototyping is twofold: to test the overarching assumptions you have made, and to learn whether this specific solution meets your design challenge and responds to the needs of the people you aim to serve.

The reason for creating a prototype is to receive helpful, relevant feedback, so you will need to determine how best to present it. Your subjects do not need to experience the concept in a refined and finished form, but you will need to achieve sufficient resolution for them to understand and evaluate it. And remember, while participant input is indispensable, they don't get to vote. Evaluating feedback is ultimately the job of the core and leadership teams.

Questions to consider

Here are some questions you should consider when preparing to test your prototype:

- Consider the setting.
  Can you test it in context, or would a more informal setting be more appropriate?

- Test your assumptions.
  What is the most important idea you need to test? What questions do you want to ask your subjects?

- Engage users and experts in the feedback process.
  Who would you like to learn from? Include people who you met during your research as well as new participants.

- Observe body language.
  What clues do the person's facial expressions or actions provide about how they are feeling while giving you this feedback?

- Look for the issue behind the issue.
  If your subjects get hung up on a small detail, for example the color, they may be harboring reservations about a larger issue. How might you probe to uncover the wider issue?

- Insist upon candor.
  "Don't worry about offending us. We want to hear everything you like and don't like about this idea. This will help us make it better." How might you create a safe environment for freeflowing feedback?

You may find it helpful to build a short discussion guide to focus your questions to your users about your prototype.

Open, general questions

WARM UP ABOUT THE CONTEXT OF THE USER YOU ARE SPEAKING WITH.
"HOW LONG HAVE YOU WORKED HERE?" "CAN YOU TELL ME ABOUT YOUR JOB?" "WHAT DOES A TYPICAL DAY LOOK LIKE?"

Search for stories

ASK THE USER TO TELL YOU ABOUT THEIR INTERACTIONS IN THE PROBLEM SPACE.
"CAN YOU SHARE AN EXAMPLE OF WHAT A GREAT DAY LOOKS LIKE?" ..."HOW ABOUT A BAD DAY?" "PLEASE TELL ME A BRIEF STORY ABOUT YOUR EXPERIENCE WITH (YOUR OPPORTUNITY AREA)."

Deep, specific questions about the idea

NOW IS THE TIME TO GO INTO THE SPECIFICS OF THE PROPOSED SOLUTION.

"WHAT EXCITES YOU MOST ABOUT THIS IDEA, AND WHY?"

"IF YOU COULD CHANGE ONE THING, WHAT WOULD IT BE?"

"WHAT WOULD YOU LIKE TO IMPROVE ABOUT THIS IDEA?"

"WHAT IDEAS DO YOU HAVE TO ADDRESS THIS PROBLEM?"

How to capture feedback

1. Provide a welcoming environment

   When setting up feedback sessions, it is important to welcome the participants in. If you are meeting with nurses, don't just intercept them on the unit. Consider welcoming them with coffee, cupcakes and a casual, collegial environment.

2. Set expectations

   People will likely be reluctant to criticize your hard work, so it's important to set expectations for your feedback capture session.

   Emphasize that these ideas are still in the making, and depend upon critical input to get stronger and better. If your audience feels you are showing ideas to which you are committed, the tone of the meeting can easily become contentious. Create an environment that says that you are not trying to impress anyone; you are working together to solve a problem.

   Introduce your prototype as a "rough sketch" that you've prepared in order to test an underlying idea. Make it clear that the idea development is still in progress, that you have not invested heavily in your prototype, that you want their honest feedback, and that you are inviting them to participate in shaping the ideas.

3. Show, don't tell

   Whether you arrange a role-play or interaction with an artifact, be creative about how to engage your end users with your prototypes. Hand sketches are great to convey that the ideas aren't done yet. Make them scrappy, but capture the sense of process by organizing them well.

   Don't just simulate the device, but provide enough context to make it plausible (bring in a baby doll if it's a neonatal situation or a wheelchair if it's a geriatric situation).

Having simple prototyping materials on hand. Tape, markers, and an x-acto knife, for example, will allow you to change key features quickly. These will help shift the conversation beyond the use of the device to the journey itself.

And never show up with only one prototype; come prepared with multiple directions to fuel a productive discussion.

4. Capture
Listen, take notes, and take photos of people interacting with your prototypes. Encourage participants to modify on the fly with you to make them better.

Don't spend time explaining or defending your prototypes; they are simply springboards for conversation to make your ideas better! If someone asks you, "Does it do ____?" or "Why does it have _____?", turn that question back on them: "What would you want that to do?" or "Why would having ____ matter or not matter to you?" Keep digging for insight. Keep asking why.

5. Reflect
After hosting a feedback session, sit with your team and story share. You can use the headings on the following page to capture what you learned.

6. Iterate
Revise your prototype; add variations on a theme. Consider additional constraints or limitations and design for them. Do this as many times as possible!

Types of things to consider in consequent iterations:

FEATURES TO KEEP	FEATURES TO INCREASE/ADD
FEATURES TO DECREASE/STOP	THE MOST IMPORTANT ELEMENTS TO MAKE YOUR IDEA A SUCCESS
QUESTIONS TO EXPLORE	NEW IDEAS TO CONSIDER

Step 6-3 Refine the concept

Iterate and refine until you are satisfied that you're ready to carry your idea forward.

As you evolve concepts through various prototypes, each expression of the initial ideas will increase in levels of refinement as you move toward an integrated, systemic view of a solution. You will be sharing fewer and fewer prototypes but with greater confidence and precision. This iterative process of prototype-feedback-refine enables the team to converge on one or two ideas that will be taken forward to pilot in patient care settings.

Reality check

The second filter we want to apply is whether the ideas that have emerged will be responsive to your design challenge. Discovery Design moves in divergent and convergent phases, and it is here that we want to do a spot check. Use these questions as inspiration:

What is the real need you are looking to address? (HMW...)

How does that need relate to your design challenge? (Point of View)

What gets users excited about it? (Use a quote!)

What unknowns remain about your idea? What do you want to know?

How else might you address your users' needs?
(Evidence-based tool? Other prototype? Existing solution?)

What are the biggest barriers/challenges you are facing with your idea?

Use the reality check to help you determine whether you should keep pursuing the current direction, emphasize some other aspect of the idea, or develop some other ideas. Prototyping is all about pivoting sooner to succeed faster! If the current direction has promise, keep going!

Use the guardrails of good design

Up until this point, we've been exploring many different directions and looking to test not so much the "thing" as much as the idea behind the "thing." But as we move forward to testing new concepts in a live environment, we want to make sure our ideas are as effective as possible and that we have avoided some common design traps.

> "When you have trouble with things—whether it's figuring out whether to push or pull a door or the arbitrary vagaries of the modern computer and electronics industries—it's not your fault. Don't blame yourself; blame the designer."
>
> — Donald Norman, *The Design of Everyday Things*

Over the years, human factors, ergonomics, safety science, and product design specialists have developed universal, research-based principles for ensuring that solutions work for their intended purpose and don't lead to unnecessary errors. These principles could help guide your design solutions and may be used as a checklist for refining your idea. As you go down the list, think: How might I improve the concept?

Keep it simple

Whether you are dealing with a product, a service, or an environment, reduce the number of steps to the minimum necessary to achieve the desired result. Avoid feature creep!

Make it visible

Avoid hidden functions and incorporate your solution into people's existing workflow. Critical information should be placed where it can be viewed by everyone who needs to see it.

Rely on intuition rather than memory

Avoid the need for memorization by breaking a procedure into simple steps. Provide a diagram. Use an acronym. Checklists, storyboards, and arrows are powerful tools.

Reduce cognitive load

Hospitals are already noisy and cluttered environments. If you must add something, try to take two things away!

Provide feedback

Sending back information about what action has been accomplished assures confirmation and avoids missteps. Always ask how people will know they've done the right thing. Avoid situations where they have to constantly monitor if something is working.

Make it usable

Ensure that your solution will work for all the shapes, sizes, strengths, and capacities of the people who will use it. Design out ways in which people could get hurt or injured, or as a last resort, clearly highlight them. Consider factors such as control, cognition, visibility, hearing, fatigue, odor, taste, tangibility, availability and reliability.

Make it sustainable

Every solution must be sustainable over the long term in light of people, time, and resource constraints. Ask how your solution will work under stress or in an emergency.

Restrict options; use forcing functions

Restrict functions to avoid errors, mistakes, or undesired actions. Always ask, "How might someone break this?" "How might someone make an error when using this?" There's a reason why there are different-sized plug holes on the anesthesia machine—to prevent placing leads in the wrong socket.

Increase consistency

Design interfaces have similar operations and use similar elements for achieving similar tasks. For instance, make sure that medication vials are always colored and stored in the same way.

Include redundancies

If the primary mechanism for a desired action, behavior, or outcome falters, does your solution provide a back-up system or trigger that highlights the gap and assures performance of the necessary steps?

Modularity

If one part of your solution fails, will the other elements continue to operate?

Avoid work-arounds

Rather than accept an unsafe or undesirable process or outcome, and develop a solution that works around it, change the system, product, or process itself. If possible, work to eliminate the risk itself rather than design around it. Remove steps rather than add them.

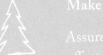

Make it natural

Assure that there are natural relationships between controls and their effects and that they conform to familiar norms of design; for example, green should always mean "go," and pill bottles should always open counterclockwise.

Provide cues and clues

The solution should contain obvious cues for how it should be used. If someone completely foreign to your project doesn't know how to interact with something you have created, there is probably room for improvement. This might be done via signs, pop-ups, diagrams, or arrows.

"There are two ways of constructing a… design: one way is to make it so simple that there are obviously no deficiencies and the other way is to make it so complicated that there are no obvious deficiencies."

— C.A.R. Hoare, Cambridge University.

Conduct a risk assessment

Building on the design principles above, to ensure that your design will work in the high-risk, highly regulated hospital environment, you will need to engage experts from various departments. In addition to design conventions and usability considerations, you will also need to be mindful of the plural risks specific to healthcare environments. These considerations are many, and may include:

- Local/State/Federal legal, regulatory, or ethical issues
- Accreditation and licensure
- Employee safety, unionization
- Patient safety, employee safety, and infection control
- Space, tools, and materials
- Use of intellectual property
- Warranties and guarantees
- Environment and context
- Partnerships, vendors, and union contracts
- Hospital policies
- Patient privacy, human-subjects research, collection and use of data
- Political or social climate
- Additional risks that you may be introducing to the system

We suggest you engage your senior stakeholders to help determine the extent and rigor of risk analysis you should undertake before implementing your idea in the care environment. This simple approach can get you started:

1. Identify: Gather your team and brainstorm how your design or implementation might fail, or result in harm to people or the organization. Use the list above as inspiration.
2. Assess: For each failure mode, note the 5 Whys (What, Why, Who, Where, and How) and generate estimates from 1 to 10 of the likelihood that the failure might occur (frequency) and the magnitude of impact (severity).

Failure Mode	Frequency	Severity	Comments

3. Frame: Plot failure modes on the following graph based on how likely a particular failure might eventuate, and the impact of that failure on the project.

4. Mitigate: Generate mitigation strategies and use the table and graph to share your initial analysis with your stakeholders. Gather their feedback and determine appropriate steps. You may be ready to move forward. You will likely have several failure modes to address; you may require additional expertise.

5. Final check: Prior to moving forward in the live environment, conduct a final check with your key stakeholders. Explain the final design (using your storyboard), report on your updated risk assessment, gather any feedback, and seek their approval to move forward.

6. Monitor and react: As you implement your solution, monitor performance against the failure modes you have identified and act accordingly.

Step 6-4 Share the concept

Bring your idea to life.

Now that you have converged on one (or a small number) of systemic concepts, supported by multiple rounds of prototyping and feedback, it is time to gather the organization's commitment and resources to launch a pilot in a real care environment.

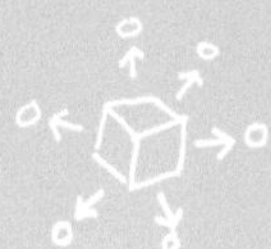

Story

In a recent project, we prepared a high-touch storyboard to describe a new system for enabling better collaboration and communication between nurses and pharmacists. We included the project goals, provided several panels describing how the solution might work, and a description of the research project that would be required to validate the idea before launching a pilot.

Virtual Pharmacist

Improve the value and effectiveness of communication between pharmacy and nursing.

- Reduce distractions and burden on pharmacy
- Improve information flows between pharmacy and nursing
- Support nurses in medication administration

ENHANCE COMMUNICATION

- A live person to contact when a nurse has a question/concern related to medications.

TRIAGE QUESTIONS

- Question types can be triaged by nurse for the most rapid answer.
- Simple pharmacy and logistics questions are answered immediately while scheduled times available for specialists.

LEVERAGE EXPERTISE

- The expert can answer questions about medication interactions, dosage, allergies, etc.
- The pharmacist can immediately process drug changes and route for MD approval if needed.

ON THE SAME PAGE

- Pharmacist can share screen, including the iVent screen that may contain valuable information about change in prescription.
- A progress bar shows where in the system an ordered med is with an ETA.

BUILDING BRIDGES

- System builds trust and enhances communication between nursing staff and pharmacy teams.
- Improving information flow enhances patient care and improves medication safety.

PILOT OVERVIEW

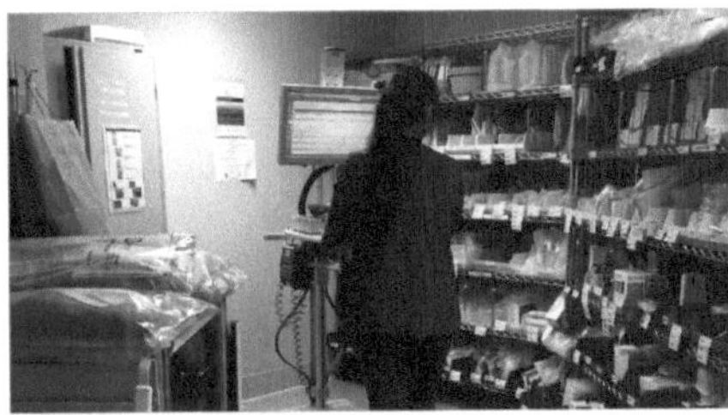

- Uncover the types of questions nurses ask pharmacists and time taken to respond.
- Create time and budget for a pharmacist to participate in the prototype.
- Socialize with pharmacists to identify volunteers to take part in pilot.

- Set up Skype station in a medication room. Define office hours.
- To measure behavior change, define a single month prototype period with periodic reviews.
- Co-host with Innovence Lab staff.

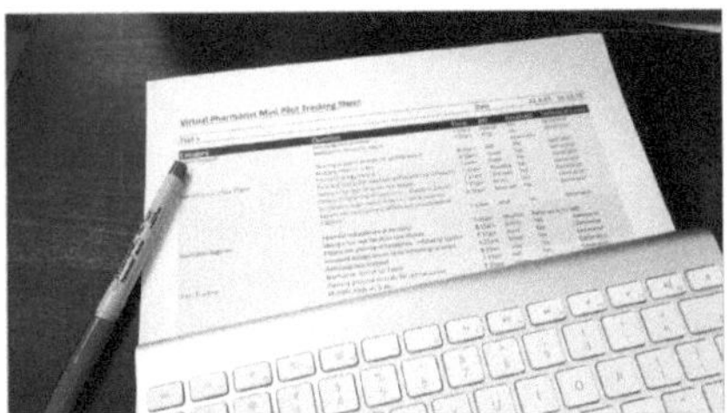

- Log the types of questions that the pharmacists receive and see how the questions evolve over time.
- Measure impact on pharmacy/nurse relationships.
- Understand common causes for late meds.

Create a concept storyboard

A storyboard is a great tool for communicating your tested and refined idea—whether a product, process, or experience—quickly and efficiently, and will highlight gaps you will need to work on. Think of it like a comic strip: What are the key moments? How do people first encounter it? How do they interact with it? What does it do? What is the hand-off moment or conclusion? Using the worksheet on the following page, create your storyboard: use diagrams, stick figures, and headlines. Provide a short description below each box.

Take a breath!

You now have a concept that has been iterated and shared with your target audience and a clear rationale to explain why it is important and valuable. After multiple rounds of iteration you will have learned an enormous amount about the people, systems, and technology that may have caused the problems you are grappling with, and that the concept that has emerged looks very different than what you anticipated. Getting you to this point has required an intense period of activity and commitment. Celebrate that!

But you are not yet done. Having experimented with the idea in safe settings, gathered feedback, and refined the concept, you are now ready to pilot it, prove it, and spread it. These are the next phases of Discovery Design.

The coming stages are characterized by building organizational confidence in your lead concepts and gathering the resources required to implement it. The distance left to travel is determined by external factors: how systemic your concept is, what technology changes are implied, and the degree of change of clinical practice that it requires.

Whereas the project to date may have been brief, it may take months or even years before it is fully implemented and becomes "business as usual." In our experience, any new concept gets implemented progressively as data accumulates and evidence grows. Our final chapters deal with piloting your idea and spreading it throughout your organization.

CONCEPT NAME:

DESCRIPTION:

AIM STATEMENT:

MOMENT 1

DESCRIPTION

MOMENT 2

DESCRIPTION

MOMENT 3

DESCRIPTION

MOMENT 4

DESCRIPTION

MOMENT 5

DESCRIPTION

MOMENT 6

DESCRIPTION

Pilot

"A design isn't finished until somebody is using it."

—Brenda Laurel

Seeing a fresh new idea evolve into a product, plan, or policy that creates lasting impact is the high-water mark of Discovery Design, the reason why we do what we do. Here, the rubber meets the road! In this phase, you will learn how to introduce a new idea into the live environment and how to tell if it's working. Once you have successfully piloted it in real-world settings, you will be ready to spread it across your organization, and even beyond.

Process steps

7-1. Develop a pilot strategy

Many prototypes lead to several pilots.

7-2. Develop a measurement strategy

Demonstrate the impact.

7-3. Launch pilots

Let's get tactical.

7-4. Evaluate your idea

Is it desirable? Feasible? Viable? Achievable?

Step 7-1 Develop a pilot strategy

Many prototypes lead to several pilots.

A prototype, as we have seen, is a way of visualizing how a solution might behave in the real world; it is purposefully fast, cheap, rough, and iterative. A pilot, by contrast, is a sustained, fully executed engagement, the purpose of which is to find out how and whether a concept will work with existing staff, space, and resources. You carve out a safe space with friendly allies and grow and scale it from there.

When do we stop prototyping and start piloting?

Before every pilot, there are many prototypes and many rounds of iteration. To move from prototype to pilot, you will need to meet three conditions:

1. You have established a sufficient level of performance and safety to permit real-life usage.
2. You have secured sufficient resources (money, time, people) to develop a robust, sustainable version of your idea.
3. You have built an appropriately broad community of support, including leadership, that understands and supports your efforts.

The purpose of a pilot is to determine what is required to move an idea from concept to full implementation. It's best accomplished in successive phases, starting small and expanding over time. The key question at this point of the process is always, "How might we validate this concept?"

In the Discovery Design process, we have found it useful to break the pilot phase into three distinct stages—lo-fi, alpha, and beta.

> "When I'm working on a problem, I never think about beauty. I think only how to solve the problem. But when I have finished, if the solution is not beautiful, I know it is wrong."
>
> —R. Buckminster Fuller

Lo-fi pilot: Learning

A low-fidelity pilot offers a chance to deploy your idea in the real world for a period of time—possibly a few hours, sometimes several days or even weeks. In the lo-fi mode, we communicate very quickly that the concepts we are testing are only for learning and do not reflect the final solution.

Until now, your prototypes have served only to visualize and communicate your idea. A low-fidelity pilot gives you a chance to test your assumptions and see how your proposed solutions might work in the real world.

A lo-fi solution pilot typically involves a few users (2 to 5 people) over a short time period (2 to 3 days) and is the leanest and cheapest version of the idea you can meaningfully implement. This may very well be little more than the prototype you developed in the previous phase! While the solution itself is tentative, the environment is real.

Participants should be drawn from the inner circle that has been part of the idea generation and co-creation process. Stay close to them as they use or interact with the new idea within their context and workflows, and improvise improvements in real time. Observe the system surrounding the new idea and take note of the questions and roadblocks that come up.

Story

In one of our projects, the team was testing an external medical device that was worn by patients on the torso with adhesive to the skin. The project team had sought IRB approval and then went out to real patients to see how they were dealing with the frequently disposable portion of the device (2 to 3 days), vs. the somewhat reusable portion (7 days). The interviews took place in the patients' homes. During the interviews, the team realized that the patients didn't know how to use the accompanying smartphone app—a critical element of the system that the company and the team had assumed had been properly explained! The take-away was the importance of doing scrappy prototypes before taking major steps such as seeking IRB approval. In this case, the physical device could have easily been mocked-up using, for example, Lego blocks and Velcro.

"Innovation = creativity × implementation"

—Robert Sutton

Story

In a project for a pharmaceutical client, the design team handed off a functioning prototype of a self-injection pen that had been favorably reviewed by patients. Key to its success was that it was small, simple, and user friendly. The client passed along the design to an implementation partner for "completion." Months passed and the project team assumed that all was well. When the final prototype for design arrived, it had grown by 50% in all dimensions. The client was unhappy, the design team was unhappy, and the implementation partner insisted that it had done no wrong. The design team worked diligently with all parties, redesigning the device with constant feedback from users. Through successive prototypes and low-fi pilots, the final version was even smaller than the original prototype. This involved considerable work, but as agents of change, it was necessary for the design team to provide intensive practical support to ensure that the original design intent was preserved.

Alpha pilot: Refining

In the next phase, which we call an "alpha pilot," we test the solution with people who may not have been part of the ideation and co-creation process. The alpha pilot may involve 10 to 20 participants and extend over a period of 1 to 2 weeks. This group might include physicians, nurses, or other healthcare professionals, with the understanding that their input will evolve the idea.

This is a first chance to gather substantive feedback from both staff and patients and to use this to assess whether the idea has validity and potential.

An alpha pilot unfolds in a controlled environment, such as a section of the care area where routine procedures take place and mistakes will not have a significant impact. A controlled setting is not subject to sudden outside influences or unacceptable risk. Bear in mind that you are trying to give your pilot the best chance of succeeding, not simulating the level of performance in a realistic usage scenario.

At this stage, you must expect tweaks as you test your assumptions. You might find that you need to adjust your idea to existing workflows, or you might discover hidden constraints; unexpected stakeholders may appear.

You should be collecting data in the form of observations, surveys, and diagrams, but recognize that they are still preliminary. Remain focused on your central concept and don't get bogged down in trying to measure everything possible.

Beta pilot: Testing

You will now move to beta testing, where the focus is real-world experience and gathering the evidence that will be required to justify the move to deployment. This is a controlled exercise in which you prove that your idea has value and deserves to be launched and scaled.

A beta pilot should be aligned with your existing change management process and conducted according to its protocols. The outcome of this step is defined entirely by what those in management expect to see if they are to make decisions under normal circumstances.

The principal objective of a beta pilot is to collect evidence that can be used to sell the idea to the organization and establish its value against competing priorities. A beta pilot involves many users—perhaps 20 to 60—over an extended period that may be 2 to 6 weeks. Your test group should include a portion of the user population that is representative of the whole.

Whereas the alpha pilot is deployed in a relatively controlled environment, the beta pilot tests your solution in the real world. Does it survive under pressure? Do people forget to use it, or is it adopted only by those who are already sympathetic? A beta pilot takes place in its expected context.

Can you take your hands off the wheel? If your idea is robust, you should expect only minor refinements. For this phase, you should be generating policies, procedures, and instructions that you expect real-world users to refer to and employ. You will also need to prove that it works and to develop qualitative and quantitative measures of improvement. Finally, you will need to determine how management will audit the process over time.

Story

Pilots can be very effective at gathering momentum towards full implementation of your idea. In a self-harm reduction project, one of our colleagues reported that the strong leadership interest and support they had at the beginning of the project had waned to become passive at best. The team was worried that they would never receive the necessary support for implementation. However, as the team reported on impact through the low-fi, alpha, and beta phases, leadership interest started to reignite. As sustained reductions in self-harm incidents were observed, the team was pleasantly surprised when they were asked to scale the solution across a second wave of units and then, as an urgent priority, on all inpatient units.

Story

In a healthcare organization in which the word "pilot" was associated with formal implementation, one of our partners elected to call the project a "Scrappy Innovation Project" (SIP). This new language was effective in getting beyond the usual "yea or nay" association with pilots and encouraged the loose, iterative culture we employ in Discovery Design.

Before you begin

Almost every activity in healthcare organizations is regulated; we are dealing with vulnerable populations in an extremely high-risk environment where well-intended initiatives can have catastrophic outcomes. Before inserting new tools, processes, or interactions in a live environment, make sure you have the approval of the relevant experts at your organization. Project teams need to take the utmost care in ensuring compliance with organizational, ethical, and regulatory policies. We recommend you always consult with your compliance department in regard to issues of privacy, infection control, patient safety, and human resources.

Learn your organization's decision criteria

Change management and quality improvement systems vary enormously by institution. It is therefore essential to understand your institution's decision-making criteria if you are to justify wide implementation. Each pilot exists in order to enable decision making and to justify the resources required to move to the next stage.

Before you embark, your team must understand what your stakeholders are looking for and present your strategy to them. Your organization will have a comfort level in regard to new initiatives. Think through the following questions before launching a pilot.

- **What sorts of stories will your leaders respond to?**
- **What evidence will you need to produce?**
- **After implementation, what value needs to be created so that the program doesn't fade or regress to the status quo?**

A key point of inspiration is to find out about other projects that were widely adopted. How did those teams approach the pilot process? Sometimes rigorous "proof" is needed. Sometimes an idea will take flight because its value is self-evident. Do your homework.

Step 7-2 Develop a measurement strategy

Demonstrate the impact.

Measurement for the purposes of lo-fi pilots can usually proceed using the same principles you developed in prototyping. However, as you move toward the alpha and beta pilots you will need to be thoughtful about the approach you will take to evaluate your solution.

Why measure?

Does your solution make care safer? Does it improve efficiencies? Is it really an improvement? How do you know?

Sometimes, the value of an idea will be so obvious to everyone that implementation is purely tactical and you don't need to get bogged down in generating "proof." More often, you will have to demonstrate that your new solution improves upon the current state. This requires discernment. What can be measured and what should be measured are two very different questions.

In Discovery Design, measurement can help you as follows:

1. Identify problems to solve or opportunities to pursue.
2. Understand the problem space in greater detail.
3. Evaluate solutions and demonstrate the value created.
4. Build a business case to justify further resource investment.

Measurement will help you determine whether your project is ready and will allow your organization to decide whether to launch it into the world. Perhaps you missed something. Perhaps you've learned something completely new and need to go back and refine some aspect of your idea. Maybe it's simply a matter of prototyping a different direction. There is no point executing a bad idea. At every step, we should collect only the minimum necessary as appropriate to convince ourselves and others that the idea should be moved towards implementation.

What is your intent?

The intent and purpose of your pilot will greatly drive the level of evidence required to establish that your idea should be implemented. Another way of saying this is that the questions you want to answer will drive the methods you use to evaluate your solutions. The following framework is adapted from Solberg, et al., 1997:

1. Improvement: Improving processes, services, and tools

Discovery Design projects typically focus on improving the human experience and performance outcomes in healthcare systems. If circumstances enable you to make a change as part of ongoing operations activities without formal permission or if your stakeholders or the subject matter do not require rigorous analysis of impact, all you need is the minimum necessary to establish that the changes you're proposing are an improvement over the status quo. Don't spend time and resources on elegant study design if you don't need it.

2. Accountability: Communicating impact

If you do need to defend your proposal in the form of a presentation, media release, or quality improvement paper, you will need to collect sufficient data to tell a powerful story that aligns with your organization's evaluation and that can hold up under external review. It does not need to be airtight, but it will need to go beyond quotes and anecdotes.

If your intent is for decision makers to direct resources to your solution, it will likely be necessary to produce evidence that benefits will exceed the costs of implementation and maintenance. In that case, a solid business case may be necessary.

3. Research: Generating new knowledge

If the goal of your project is to test a hypothesis, generate new, generalizable knowledge, or involves regulated activities such as an alteration to the diagnosis and treatment of disease, you will need to use formal scientific methodologies and to draw upon deep expertise in research study design.

Decisions about care need to be evidence-based, so depending on the scope of your project, you may need to employ a high level of rigor. This may involve a robust understanding of human-subjects research regulations, IRB processes, informed consents, and protections for vulnerable populations—all of which are beyond the scope of this handbook. For an extensive discussion of improvement science, human-subjects research, and healthcare product or drug evaluation, refer to the Institute for Healthcare Improvement (IHI), The Agency for Healthcare Research and Quality (AHRQ), The Food and Drug Administration (FDA), and the Office for Human Research Protections (OHRP) of the U.S. Department of Health and Human Services (HHS).

Cautionary note

Leaders tend to ask for research-level data in excess of what is possible or necessary. It is essential that you align expectations in terms of what can be established and what types of qualitative and quantitative data should be collected given your goals and resources. Consider the following:

Appropriateness

While your hope may be that the solutions you generate may one day benefit the world, the first goal of Discovery Design projects is to improve the local setting. If the decision to implement your solution does not require evidence of generalizability (namely, that it will work in settings beyond your setting), try to resist the temptation to subject your efforts to these standards over other evidence-based approaches that may be less familiar, which we will explore in the next section.

Time lag and rarity

Projects that are designed to prevent medical errors or lawsuits may not be able to show impact within the timeline allowed for you to pilot given the time lag between improvements and anticipated outcomes. Be aware that the data that motivated the search for a solution may not be the data you use to validate it.

Proving the negative

In the area of risk and safety, a goal of our efforts is to prevent serious but rare events from occurring; the data points of safety are few. Over the course of a pilot, it may be difficult to prove that something would have happened but didn't as a result of your efforts.

Confounding variables

In healthcare organizations, there are many confounding variables between the intervention and the positive improvements we hope for. The well-known Hawthorne Effect, observation biases, small data sets, and subjectivity all make assertions as to "proof" of impact on clinical outcomes difficult to sustain.

Resource constraints

Statistically significant time-based studies, observations, surveys, and other formal improvement indicators may simply be out of reach given the time and resources available to your team. You may therefore need to explain that you will employ other appropriate indicators to justify the validity and effectiveness of your solution.

How will you evaluate impact?

The Institute for Healthcare Improvement asks the fundamental question: How do we know change has been an improvement? If your project is subject to formal regulatory or ethical oversight, whether by nature or due to your intent, you will need to consult with necessary experts and likely use a formal scientific protocol. In Discovery Design, we are primarily concerned with whether the changes we are making are improving performance and outcomes in the local setting. To evaluate and validate the efficacy of Pilot solutions, we use the following approaches derived from the fields of human factors engineering and quality improvement:

1. User engagement.
2. User validation.
3. Design quality.
4. Reliability.
5. Performance improvement.

1. User engagement

Such is the confidence of human factors engineers in the human-centered design process that a key indicator of design quality is the extent to which the solutions development process involves the robust engagement of end users at every stage. By contrast, a key indicator of poor design is if the intended beneficiaries of a process are not involved.

Evidence that end users have validated insights from your research, helped define the problem to which you directed ideation efforts, contributed to solutions generation and prototyping, and participated heavily in refining and piloting solutions are primary indicators of the quality of your design.

You should be able to answer a resounding "yes!" to the questions, "did you involve patients?" "Did you speak to the frontline?" "How about the pharm-techs?" "Did marketing review this?"

Photos, quotes, and testimonies are all good indicators that you have not rushed or failed to take account of a key stakeholder group. For example, in the course of a medication safety project, we heard the following:

> *"We should do more projects like this. This is fun."–Nurse*
>
> *"Improvement work angers me. It always fails. These people are telling me to do my job when they don't know how to do it. But, when we do include the frontliners in the process and get feedback from the nurses on an ongoing basis, it works. This is real empowerment."–Nurse manager*
>
> *"This is exactly the kind of work we need to be doing. What can we do to support it?"–Chief Nursing Officer*
>
> *"The frontline guided the process. We built from their ideas and incorporated their feedback. They set the goal and decided the best way to get there."–Nurse educator*

2. User validation

Human-centered design methodologies collect insights from people in real-world settings, remain close to them along the way, and conduct quick iterations in response to qualitative learning. End users are experts in their own experience. Therefore, a second indicator of design quality is the direct feedback from people as they utilize the new solution. Does it work for them? Evidence of impact often comes in the form of qualitative feedback and personal stories. For example, in the same medication safety project, the design team heard the following statements:

> *"Oh no! I think I've distracted nurses in the past. I had no idea."–Child's Mother*
>
> *"This is wonderful information, for us but also for visitors. Make it into a big poster and hang it on the wall in the room so the rest of the family knows what's going on."–Child's Father*
>
> *"This is great. It usually takes time before nurses get to know me. Here we have it all on the same page. I want this during admissions."–14-year old patient*
>
> *"There's no learning curve. I saw it and knew what to do. Handing a tray over to the family makes this process feel professional and important."–Nurse*

Here, success is determined by users in the system. If the consensus is that the solution is an improvement, and circumstances permit, performance is "proven" and the process stops. Implementation equals success!

3. Design quality

A powerful indicator of design quality is the extent to which the solution conforms to the evidence-based design principles outlined in Step 6-3. These principles derive from a deep tradition of research into how to design high-performing work systems, products, and services that work for people and increase their well-being. Embedding these in the solution is of itself a primary indicator that the solution will achieve its intended effect. As an example, the design quality of a solution may be plotted on a scale that is predictive of its reliability to perform as desired.

An undesigned system.
The system relies on memory or judgment to action a particular task as desired, creating wide variation in practice and outcomes.

Standardization.
Desired behaviors are codified in education, training, aids, policies, or otherwise. However, the design still relies on humans to remember to behave as desired.

Feedback.
The design provides users with feedback as to when they have successfully completed or executed a particular task; however, the manner of execution is up to the user.

Forcing functions.
The design makes it almost impossible to complete the wrong action or the majority of critical tasks are automated upon trigger.

Automation.
A variety of tasks are completed by machine or triggered by machine; the human is not involved.

Automation promises higher reliability due to consistent performance compared to humans, particularly for repetitive, simple, and highly standardized tasks. However, human intuition and abilities to recognize patterns and quickly adapt to unique circumstances still outperform technology in complex settings, especially in healthcare. Therefore, the automation must be applied with great care. New trends and applications of machine learning may change the landscape again, depending on how successfully technologies outperform humans when coping with complexity.

Story

A hospital employed a decision aid tool that required doctors to give patients a barcode that they would use to log into an online system when they went home. The information provided had been separately researched to determine efficacy, but the design left customers confused and frustrated, and very few patients completed the program. Reliability measures should have been used to establish that the system worked as desired within the setting.

4. Reliability

Establishing causal relationships in complex systems is fraught with difficulties. Limited data sets, myriad confounding variables, measurement biases, and time lags limit the efficacy of performance measurement approaches. In the world of design, often the best way to assess the performance and whether a solution is likely to achieve its ultimate aim is the degree to which the idea functions as desired for a specific period of time. This is known as reliability.

Total reliability means that the idea functions as desired 100% of the time. Reliability is expressed by reference to a failure rate—in other words, the number of failures per attempts in orders of magnitude from 10, 100, 1000, and onward. 10^{-1} indicates one failure out of 10 attempts, 10^{-2} indicates one failure out of 100 attempts, and so on (Boston-Fleischhauer, C., 2008; Nolan, T. et al., 2004).

For example, if as a result of your solution you increase the number of times patient medication counseling occurs within 24 hours of admission from 9 out 10 times (i.e., 10^{-1}), to 99 out of 100 times (i.e., 10^{-2}), this represents an order of magnitude increase in reliability—a powerful result! In healthcare, a performance at 10-1 is considered the bare-minimum threshold for reliability; anything less is viewed as wholly unreliable.

And how do we design our solutions to maximize reliability? Involve end users at every stage in the process and leverage evidence-based design principles in the design. You should aim to design systems that perform at 10^{-2}, 10^{-3}, and beyond. Consider that the reliability standard in aviation and nuclear power plants is 10^{-6}!

Reliability is an excellent measure if the ultimate goal of your project is to impact a data point that is not easily evaluated over the short term. If the ideas are sound, the fact that your solution provides the necessary inputs may be a high predictor of efficacy.

In adopting these concepts, use the following approach to evaluate the impact of your efforts:

1. **Evaluate the status quo**

   Assess the current state of the physical, cognitive, and organizational nature of the system (individual, team, unit, cross-organizational level) by identifying suboptimal design (of products, services, processes) by reference to human-centered design principles and the levels listed above.

2. **Use good design**

   Design or redesign the system to improve design quality and reliability following evidence-based design principles and with robust engagement of end users.

3. **Assess impact**

   Demonstrate the improvement by showing:

   - evidence of heavy user engagement throughout the process.
   - the differences in quality between pre and post redesign—for example, the use of affordances, cues and clues, simplicity, and so on
   - the degree to which your solution performs as desired (i.e., reliability).

> "'Some' is not a number and 'soon' is not a time."
>
> —Don Berwick, MD

5. Performance improvement

The Institute of Healthcare Improvement's "Model for Improvement" employs tools, many of which are simple enough to apply without training in statistics and can aid Discovery Designers in assessing their pilots.

What are you trying to accomplish?

The process starts by developing a specific aim for what you are trying to achieve that is simple, time-specific, includes numerical goals, and defines the target people or systems. For example:

> "Reduce needle sticks" is not an effective aim. "Reduce needlestick injuries in orthopedic surgery residents by 80% in six months" is much better.

> "Improve communication" is not an effective aim. A better construction would be, "Improve the recollection of the risks, alternatives, and benefits of ophthalmological procedures in patients over 65 years old by 30% by March 1."

How will you know your idea has made an improvement?

Now you need to decide what measures you will use to signal whether your solution is working to achieve your aim. Be mindful of the purpose of your project—improvement, accountability, or research. In research contexts, data collection is expensive and time-intensive. In Discovery Design, we are most interested in collecting just as much data as possible to determine whether you're making the impact you hope for.

There are three types of measures:

- **Process measures** help you capture what is happening in the system, process, or experience around your idea, which may lead to the change you are aiming for. For example, how many patients have been given instructions about how to use the app? Perhaps we can track downloads and provide a passive prompt in the EMR for every time the information was given to a patient.

- **Outcome measures** capture whether you are achieving your aim. For example, is our new app for patients to track their medications achieving our aim of increasing adherence to medication regimens for oncology patients by 20% within three months?

- **Balancing measures** are critical for capturing whether your proposed solution is resulting in unintended negative consequences. For example, is the new app increasing the burden on patients post-discharge? Perhaps we can create a pre/post survey to capture patient perceptions and confidence in their care upon discharge?

Data collection strategies

Impact can be captured by qualitative and quantitative measures of processes and outcomes. The following list contains just a few examples of tools we commonly use in Discovery Design.

Qualitative tools of collection may include:

- Interviews
- Observations
- Pre/post surveys
- Observing people in context (shadowing)

Quantitative data collection tools may include:

- Standardized surveys
- The number of downloads of an app, or forms filled out.
- Administrative data, such as the number of procedures, number and type of patients, diagnosis and procedure codes, and amounts billed.
- Medical record reviews
- GPS trackers
- Step counters

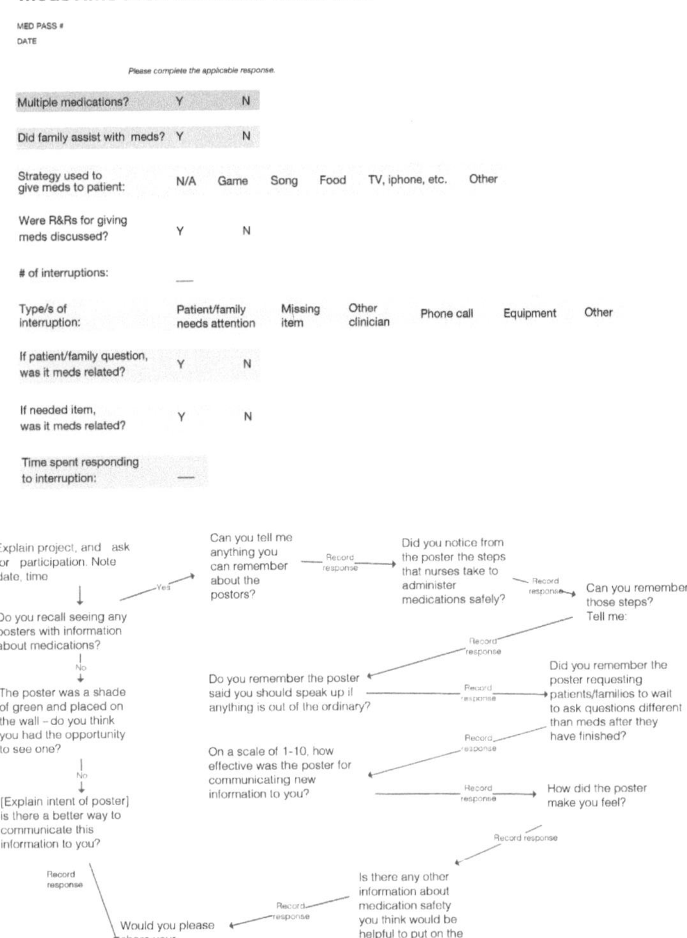

MedsTime Pre/Post Observation Tool

MED PASS #

DATE

Please complete the applicable response.

Multiple medications?	Y	N				
Did family assist with meds?	Y	N				
Strategy used to give meds to patient:	N/A	Game	Song	Food	TV, iphone, etc.	Other
Were R&Rs for giving meds discussed?	Y	N				
# of interruptions:	__					
Type/s of interruption:	Patient/family needs attention	Missing item	Other clinician	Phone call	Equipment	Other
If patient/family question, was it meds related?	Y	N				
If needed item, was it meds related?	Y	N				
Time spent responding to interruption:	__					

Example observation tool from a recent project assessing interruptions in medication administration in a pediatric context.

Explain project, and ask for participation. Note date, time

Do you recall seeing any posters with information about medications?

Yes → Can you tell me anything you can remember about the posters? → Record response → Did you notice from the poster the steps that nurses take to administer medications safely? → Record response → Can you remember those steps? Tell me: → Record response → Do you remember the poster said you should speak up if anything is out of the ordinary? → Record response → Did you remember the poster requesting patients/families to wait to ask questions different than meds after they have finished? → Record response → On a scale of 1-10, how effective was the poster for communicating new information to you? → Record response → How did the poster make you feel? → Record response → Is there any other information about medication safety you think would be helpful to put on the poster? → Record response → Would you please share your demographic information with us?

No → The poster was a shade of green and placed on the wall - do you think you had the opportunity to see one?

No → [Explain intent of poster] is there a better way to communicate this information to you? → Record response → Would you please share your demographic information with us?

Example structured interview tool for assessing the effectiveness of a new educational poster.

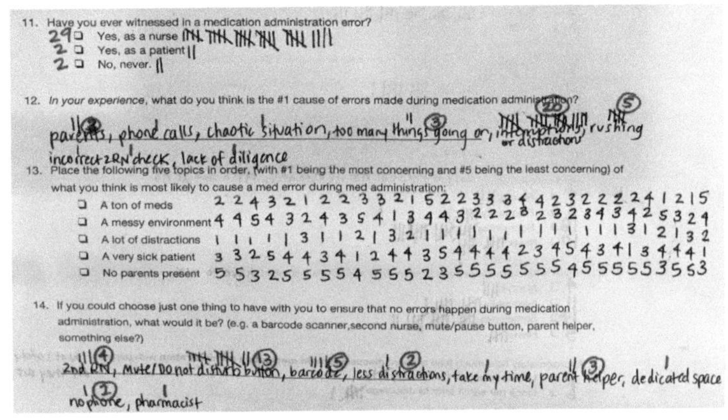

11. Have you ever witnessed in a medication administration error?
    - 29 ❑ Yes, as a nurse
    - 2 ❑ Yes, as a patient
    - 2 ❑ No, never.

12. *In your experience*, what do you think is the #1 cause of errors made during medication administration?

    parents, phone calls, chaotic situation, too many things going on, interruptions or distraction, rushing
    incorrect 2RN check, lack of diligence

13. Place the following five topics in order, (with #1 being the most concerning and #5 being the least concerning) of what you think is most likely to cause a med error during med administration:
    - ❑ A ton of meds
    - ❑ A messy environment
    - ❑ A lot of distractions
    - ❑ A very sick patient
    - ❑ No parents present

14. If you could choose just one thing to have with you to ensure that no errors happen during medication administration, what would it be? (e.g. a barcode scanner,second nurse, mute/pause button, parent helper, something else?)

    2nd RN, Mute/Do not disturb button, barcode, less distractions, take my time, parent helper, dedicated space
    no phone, pharmacist

Example extract of a survey assessing the perceptions of nurses in relation to medication errors.

There are many ways to visualize data, and you don't necessarily need to be a statistician to do so. You can look at the "charts" feature in Word or Excel to gain inspiration.

The most common tools are run charts and histograms, which are excellent for tracking data over time.

On the y-axis, note your data point, and on the x-axis, plot data over time. As a general rule, you will need 6 data points going up or going down to indicate a non-random change. However, when we get beyond 12 and 20, we can start making deeper assessments as to what is going on: Has there been a real shift to a new normal? Is there a new trend?

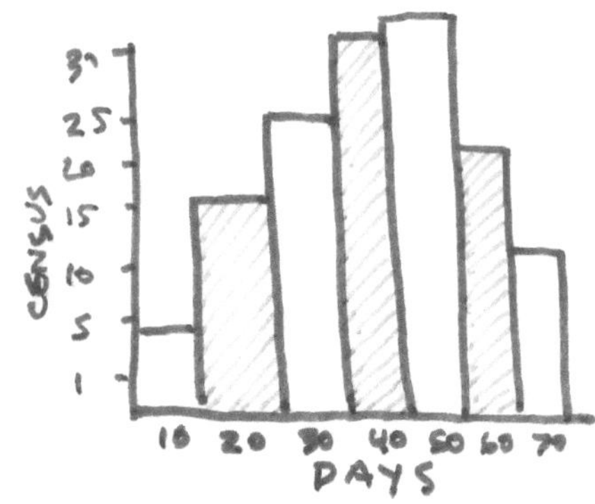

Example histogram for helping understand the distribution of continuous data such as here, the number of patients readmitted over time. This chart indicates that there were 4 readmissions within 10 days of discharge, and 15 readmissions within 20 days.

Example run chart for tracking performance over time, such here, the number of patient education tools completed.

Tips for capturing data

A few basic principles should assist in the selection, design, and use of your measurement tools:

Keep it simple

Remember, we are not looking for generalizable evidence that your solution works for all people at all times and in every situation. We are looking for the best possible solution for this context. Therefore, keep it simple. Limit the number of measurement categories and minimize the effort and time needed to capture impact. If one measure would be "amazing" but will take months to set up, find something 60% as effective that you can start capturing today. Not everything that can be measured, should be measured.

Keep it scrappy

Don't digitize data unless you have to; hand-drawn graphs and tables are easy to read and can be updated in the moment. Data collection should ideally enable you to iterate daily or weekly.

Make it visual

Plot data collection in an area where it can easily be seen by the team and in the environment where the change is being deployed. This will help keep up the momentum and excitement surrounding your project.

Make it easy

Make data collection easy for your team. Try to avoid requiring end users to perform additional tasks. Try to make data collection part of the daily routine. Are there existing systems you can leverage? Are there passive tools you can use? Further, design the tools to be easy to follow and fill out. Use a mobile app, checklist, stickers, or color codes. Be creative!

Keep it consistent

There may be information that is only usefully collected in one of the stages. However, try to compare oranges with oranges. For example, ask the same interview questions before and after implementation.

Capture lots of data points

Within the limited set of measurement categories you choose, try to capture as many data points as possible. The strongest approach is to conduct observations, structured interviews, surveys, and other measurements before implementation at regular points during your pilot and again after the solution has been embedded for some time.

While single pre and post measures may be sufficient to provide a strong indication of lasting change, you need a minimum of five to six data points; there is no maximum! In general, we aim for a minimum of 40 to 60 survey responses, observations, and structured interviews; however, recognize that these numbers are usually insufficient for statistical significance.

Limit open-ended questions

In order to efficiently measure pre and post impact, try to limit responses to "yes" and "no" questions. There will be opportunities for collecting open-ended feedback later on.

Engage a variety of stakeholders

To develop a robust indication of impact, try to capture data from the multiple stakeholders your solution touches. Collecting fewer data points from a variety of users is better than lots of data points from only one stakeholder group.

Don't forget empathy

Although our measurement tools may seem primarily analytical, empathy-, intuitive-, and design-driven feedback should be continuously captured as you assess impact and iterate. Data points will tell you what and when, but empathy can tell you why, and what to do next.

Each of these approaches brings value to a healthcare improvement project, and any of them may be required in context-specific institutions or organizations.

Set yourself up for success

As we learned in our discussion of empathy, the success of any new product or service depends on the responses of the people for whom it is intended. Here's a checklist of essential strategies that can help set your pilot and the people you are seeking to serve up for success:

Is the vision clear? ☐

Have the vision and goals of the project been made clear to everyone who is impacted by it? Have newsletters gone out? Have you attended staff meetings? Has leadership shown its support of the project in a video or email you can display?

A good practice is to imagine how you might introduce your new idea to people who have never heard about your project. Will they welcome an exciting new initiative or view it as another chore?

> "Poor executions invalidate good ideas."
>
> —A. Smart Innovator

Host a gathering to which you bring a few props that will stoke people's interest. You'll be surprised at the effect of a kid-sized package of candy against 30 years of clinical practice!

Have you built an unstoppable coalition of support? ☐

Although Discovery Design rests on the belief that the best ideas flow from the bottom up, you will need high-level leadership support to implement them, not to mention the various committees and gatekeepers that will need to sign off along the way. Unless you are working solely under the auspices of your sponsor, you will need strong support throughout the organization, including among people who may be unfamiliar with your project. Use the assets you have been collecting to introduce people afresh, and put yourself in the position of others when you seek their support. Look for opportunities to add value at every stage.

Executives

Executives will be your biggest allies, but bear in mind that c-suite leaders are used to making decisions and will likely have just come out of one meeting and be thinking of the next. Try to arrange an invitation to introduce the project, and keep your presentation concise. Be clear about what you want from them: "What we are hoping for from you is ..." will prove more effective than an open-ended, "What do you think?" Suggest ways in which the project might serve as an opportunity for them: Media story? Grant funding? Research study?

An excellent practice for keeping executive stakeholders engaged is to schedule a recurring monthly or quarterly meeting. This will keep all parties informed as the project moves forward and will prepare you when you meet unexpected resistance.

Mid-level partners

In our experience, it can be easy to forget the importance of mid-level partners. Any significant initiative in a healthcare organization will need firm support from multiple mid-level managers with varying degrees of expertise, influence, and authority. Invite them to your project space, make personal connections, and learn what it looks like from their perspective. Share the project journey with them, explore areas for partnership, and leave with concrete next steps. Make sure they receive your regular newsletter and that you call them out. As a general principle, share credit generously.

Committees

Committees are essential organisms within the life of any organization and of healthcare organizations in particular. When they are functioning well, they ensure that change moves smoothly and is in line with established policies and constraints. Committees may have little awareness of the background or context of your project, so it is best to engage them before making a formal presentation. Committees may view it as their job to give you direction or supervision, so you should be sure to list them as partners to demonstrate that their feedback has been integrated into your plan and has influenced its course.

Frontline champions

If you haven't done so already, now is the time to identify local champions and make them partners in rolling out the pilot. Go to them. Familiarize yourself with their workflows and learn what life is like from where they sit. Go in with an open mind even if you've spent time in similar environments. When introducing the project, make sure you can demonstrate that people on the front lines have been involved at every stage in the design of the new solution. They are the ones who will implement your idea and are critical to its success, so help them feel that you really are there to serve them—which you are! Think of ways of celebrating their contributions and sustaining their participation—for example, create a "Patient Safety Champion of the Month Award."

Discovery Design is empathy driven at every level of your organization and at every stage of your process. The best work happens when people are invested in the project and feel connected to the people driving it. Building a sincere, genuine community with people you work with is not just useful for the project, it is what the project is all about.

Are you ready? ☐

Effective pilots need focused attention and dedicated time. With all the momentum you've been building and with so many competing priorities, you will need to be sure you have allocated the time and resources necessary to carry it to completion. And if time is important, so is timing. It may be advisable to advance, delay, or modify your approach in response to leadership changes, budget cycles, building programs, and the vagaries of people's schedules All institutions are complex, and healthcare organizations are more complex than most. As frustrating as it may be, you may wish to delay the launch of your pilot if doing so will increase the likelihood of success.

Step 7-3 Launch pilots

Let's get tactical.

You are now in a position to construct your pilot strategy on the foundations you have laid.

Preparing the lo-fi strategy

It may be that the solution you are thinking of doesn't appear amenable to a live test without significant resource investment. If that is the case, gather your team for a brainstorm to see what aspects of the solution could be tested in a live pilot. What are those elements?

a. For each element, determine the most important question you need to answer to justify an alpha pilot.

b. For each question, ask what is the smallest, cheapest way it can be answered?

c. Decide where, when, and with whom can you test it.

d. Pilot!

e. Incorporate feedback and learning, and determine the users, timing, and context appropriate for the next phase.

Preparing the alpha and beta strategies

The alpha and beta pilots will need more rigor as your questions change. It's no longer a question of "Does this aspect or assumption work?", but "Does this solution work and produce its intended results?" Now is the time to bring it together. Identify the key elements that are critical to making the solution work. Now, determine your measurement strategy.

1. Determine your measurement strategy

How will you know the solution is working? How will you capture impact?

There are many ways to evaluate how and whether a proposed solution is working for the people and in the context for which it is intended. A good measurement strategy will include tactics to collect process and outcome impacts, performance targets, and plans for how to collect, analyze, and continuously monitor results.

2. Design your measurement tools

Step 1: Get together with your team and use sticky notes to create several different aim statements. Be ambitious!!

Outcome: ______________________________

To whom, what, and where: ______________

By when: ______________________________

Keep refining your aim statements until you have one (or a few). Aim statements should be inspiring and compel the team and stakeholders into action.

Step 2: Take each aim statement and brainstorm the various ways you can capture outcome, process, and balancing measures. Remember the brainstorming rules. This is a creative process, and you may find unexpected, unconventional ways of capturing impact.

Step 3: For each category of measurement, plot your ideas along a priority matrix to determine which ones meet the criteria we discussed above. Push to select the items in the top left quadrant:

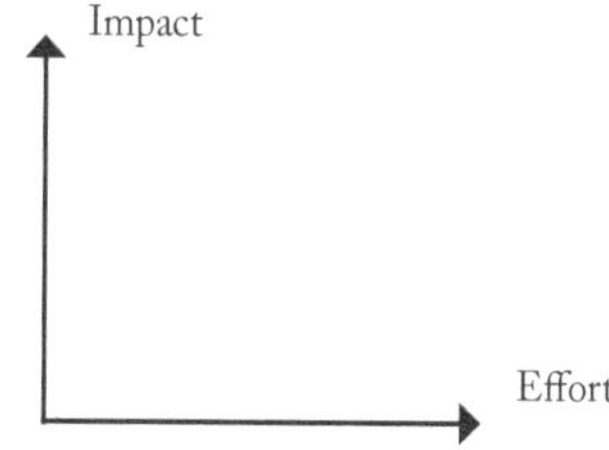

Step 4: Create your measurement tools and think about how you will use them.

Step 5: Create a space to display your measures.

Step 6: Determine who is going to collect, analyze, and own communication of data.

3. Clarify your thinking

An excellent tool borrowed from quality improvement literature is a logic model. It helps guide our thinking about how our planned activities will lead to the change we are hoping for, align the team, and expose gaps in our assumptions or resources. Below we've created an example chart. Descriptions are noted in the first row. An example from an OR surgical checklist project we conducted is listed in the second row.

Resources	Tasks	Deliverables	Short-Term Outcomes	Medium-Term Outcomes	Long-Term Outcomes
Specific list of resources available or needed to do the work: People, materials, funding, physical space.	Overview of the plan about what you intend to do with the inputs. This often exposes gaps!	Given our inputs and activities, what do we expect to produce? For whom? By when?	What changes we expect to see in the short term? This likely includes qualitative feedback in terms of knowledge, attitudes, and beliefs.	What changes we expect to see in the medium term in behaviors and processes? Here, we would hope to collect qualitative and quantitative data regarding the impact on process and outcomes.	What changes do we expect to see in the long term in terms of process, outcomes, and total value impact and return on investment?
• Program manager. • $$$$ funding. • Meeting space. • Team of volunteers.	• Collect baseline data. • Create new checklist. • Determine new workflow. • Quarterly leadership engagement meetings. • Have daily huddles. • Build new policy. • Create aids for all OR staff.	• Baseline data report by [date]. • All OR managers trained by [date]. • Chair has laid expectation by [date]. • New process, policy, aids created and disseminated.	• 40% increase in knowledge of importance of surgical checklist via survey after one month. • All members of OR team understand their role and expectations for time-out by survey after one month.	• Increase to 80% compliance of new checklist process after two months.	• Achieve 95% performance for new checklist process after six months. • Improved clinician perception of ability to "speak up" by 20% after six months. • Demonstrate an ROI of 43%.

4. Create your pilot plan

To create a robust pilot plan, use the Hopes and Fears exercise discussed in Phase 2: Prepare.

Imagine the pilot has been an unqualified success, and think about every step, stakeholder, resource, and activity you can think of that went into it.

Now imagine it as a movie script:

- How did it start?
- When did different characters come into play?
- What did they need to do or say?
- How far in advance did you need to involve them?

Then, do the same imagining that the pilot failed spectacularly. What new activities will you add to assure success?

Break the pilot process down into discrete steps that you can check off once they've been completed. Clearly note what will occur, when it will occur, who is responsible for it, what resources they will need, and how you will know it has been completed.

Pilot Plan

Project Tasks	Pilot Schedule: Week 1	Week 2	Week 3	Week 4	Week 5	Week 6	Owners and Helpers	Resources Needed	Comments and Tracking
Collect Pre-Measures	x	x					Abdul + Nick	2x iPads Camera	Update 3/14: 60x surveys completed 45x observations completed
Staff training		x					Bob + Nick	Conference room	Update 3/18: 90% complete. A few MDs were out sick. Following up direct. Update 3/21: Training complete.
Install solution		x					Bob + Nick	IT contact: John	Update 3/28: Install complete in ORs.
Monitor & refine			x				Sally + Nick		Update 4/2 OR staff enjoying first week of new tool: "This makes life easier!" OR Mgr. Minor text and size edit completed.
Collect post-measures							Sally + Nick	2x iPads Camera	Update 4/2: Sally will be out this week. Need to find a replacement.
Analyze data and prepare report							Sally + Bob	Kelly from QI	Update 3/25: Our analytics software subscription expired. We need CIO's approval. Sally is will meet with her VP to take forward. Update 4/2: no change.
Report to CMO							Bob	PPT deck	Update 3/24: CMO meeting just got moved. Finding another date. Update 4/2: no change.

Tracker: Performing Satisfactory | Requires Action | Requires Escalation

5. Create a communications tool

There is a big difference between the level of detail you need for leading the pilot and the information you should share with the wider community of stakeholders. Use empathy: Be clear about what busy people need to know and to do, and don't saddle them with minutiae. You might have different communication pieces tailored based on who they are for.

Here is a short guide for what you might want to communicate to key project partners and stakeholders. Try to fit it on one page.

Purpose	Create an aspirational, visionary headline for your project, something that will capture interest!
Sponsors	Senior executive/s with ultimate accountability for or oversight of the project.
Team	The people responsible for the day-to-day management of the project. You may also include key partners here as well. Use friendly head shots if you can, to give the project a face.
Brief background	Why is the project important? Where did it come from? Where is it going? How is it being done? Who is doing it?
Aim	What are you trying to achieve?
Indicators of impact	How are you planning to evaluate the impact of your efforts?
Pilot phases	Provide an overview of the key phases of the pilot so people know what to expect. Use a simple graphic and elaborate. We used PowerPoint's "SmartArt" function to create the one on the opposite page in under 10 minutes.

PHASE 1:
BASELINE 2 WKS

PHASE 2:
PREPARE 1 WK

PHASE 3:
IMPLEMENT 4 WKS

PHASE 4:
MEASURE 2 WKS

PHASE 5:
REVIEW 1 WK

Phase 1. Baseline

If you will be collecting baseline measures, how, when, and who will do it?

Phase 2. Prepare

Does the subject population need to be trained or introduced to the new solution before you start the pilot? How, when, and who will do it?

Phase 3. Implement

Describe how the new solution will be installed into the new environment or workflow. Provide enough detail so that people will recognize and feel comfortable with whatever changes you are making.

Phase 4. Measure

Describe how you will be capturing data. Will you be making observations, taking surveys, or doing passive surveillance? How will you collect consents from patients, families, clinicians, and others as required?

Phase 5. Review/Refine/Next steps

When does the pilot finish? What happens next?

Scope

Prepare

Discover

Synthesize

Generate

Prototype

Pilot

Spread

MedsTime!

What you need to know.

MedsTime is a nurse driven project that we are working on to improve medication safety at the bedside. The poster and brochure we have developed are designed to engage patients and families during medication administration.

What this will do for you..

During medication administration patients and families will be invited to participate, reducing unhelpful distractions and assisting nurse workflow. The medication preferences brochure will help you gather all the things you may need to help give medications, reducing the amount of trips in and out of the room.

What you need to do.

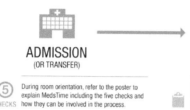

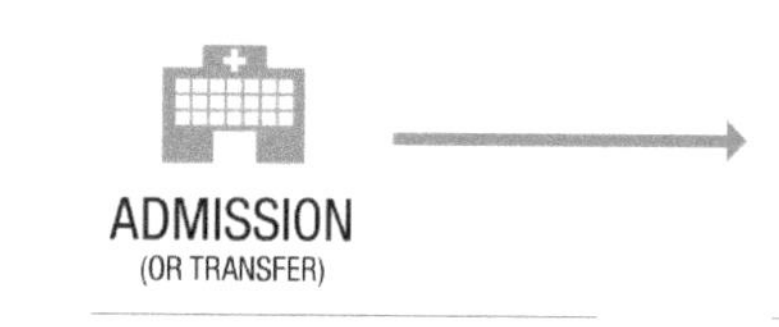

ADMISSION (OR TRANSFER)

- 5 CHECKS — During room orientation, refer to the poster to explain MedsTime including the five checks and how they can be involved in the process.
- Give parents the Medication Preferences Brochure and encourage them to fill it out. This brochure is included in the U.S.A. packet and additional copies can be found in the break room.
- Document in the "education" tab that you have taught parents about medication safety.

DURING STAY

- During safety checks, make sure the Medication Preferences Brochure is on the MedsTime clipboard and refer to it as you prepare for medication administration.
- Continue to involve patients and families during medication administration.
- During night shift, discuss with patients and families if there are any changes that need to be updated on the brochure.

AT DISCHARGE

- Invite patients and families to take the Medication Preferences Brochure home to help maintain continuity in medication administration.

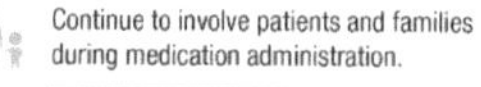

What will help you.

The Medication Preferences Brochure

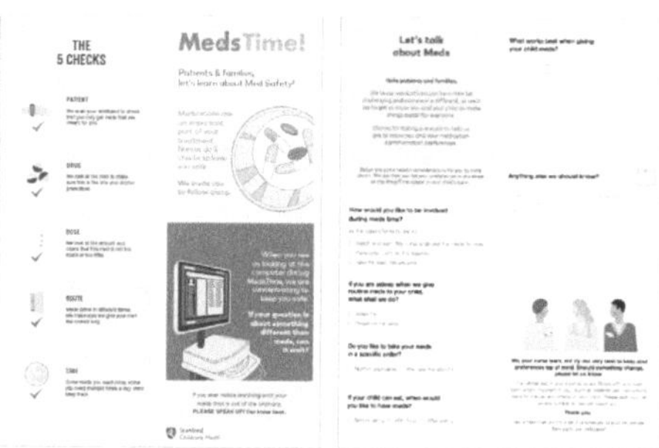

The MedsTime Poster

The MedsTime Clipboard

The people who will use the solution need to clearly understand their roles, responsibilities, and timetables. A visual aid in the form of a pamphlet, poster, wristband, or name badge are all effective approaches. Be creative!

For example, in a medication safety project, we designed the "cheat sheet" poster above and placed it in the nurses' restrooms, in the staff room, and on the project wall and pushed via email.

6. Launch pilot!

Pilots require lots of energy and attention. Block out your schedule, be present, and make sure you are available. Poor executions invalidate good ideas, so be prepared to move with speed. Depending on what phase pilot you are running—lo-fi, alpha, or beta, you should always try to hit the road running.

Look back at your team meetings in the second phase of Discovery Design. Get the team together and discuss hopes and fears, re/create a visual calendar, set a regular cadence for communications, and decide on common tools for sharing information.

7. Measure, learn, and refine

From here, your tasks will be different depending on the maturity of your pilot. In lo-fi and alpha, capture feedback at the end of each day, and use it to iterate on your core idea. If something does not work on Day 1, try a different approach on Day 2. In beta or beyond, you should be conducting regular check-ins and making minor refinements.

At every stage, be sure to document progress: stories, quotes, pictures, and anything else that can help others understand what it is that you are doing. And bring to life the insights that will inspire future directions. Be sure to capture successes as well as failures, missteps, and unintended consequences.

Be careful throughout the project to assure that you are being faithful to the design intent of the solution and evidence-based design principles.

Execute your measurement strategy. Keep it simple, use appropriate tools, and make it transparent by posting progress in areas where it will be seen by everyone. And make it visual: use graphs, tables, photographs, and quotes to tell the story.

Step 7-4 Evaluate your idea

Is it desirable? Feasible? Viable? Achievable?

The goal of the piloting stage in the discovery process is to transform a promising concept into a live solution. The reason we pilot ideas in Discovery Design is to ensure that we do not move forward with a solution that fails upon implementation.

As an idea advances toward full-scale implementation, you will need to account for the four criteria that define the best ideas:

1. **Is it desirable: Are we addressing a real need?**

   In healthcare organizations, we may be serving multiple "end users," including patients and their families, physicians and nurses, administrators, insurers, regulators, and the community at large. We must be certain that we are solving a genuine, unmet need, whether or not it is recognized as such.

2. **Is it feasible: Does it work?**

   A solution may purport to solve a problem but fail because the technology is unreliable, the design is difficult to use, or that it favors one constituency over another. To be effective, any solution must technically work in the environment and for the people for whom it is intended.

3. **Is it viable: Does it generate value over time?**

   A viable solution delivers lasting value in both human and financial terms. While many solutions may bring added value to patients, providers, and the community, there needs to be a business model that enables the program to continue. Does it create operational efficiencies? Do people continue to use it? Does it reduce harm? What's the return on investment? Is it financially sustainable?

4. **Is it achievable: Can we can get it done?**

   Sometimes the best ideas cannot be implemented because of organizational realities—such as resource allocations, internal politics, or the intangibles of talent, motivation, and energy. It's essential to account for resource constraints and shifting financial and strategic priorities. Does the organization perceive it as a priority? Has your clinic, hospital, or foundation acknowledged that the problem is important and should be solved? Does it fit within the organization's strategy or an executive's portfolio? Do the data support tangible interest and action? Is there a financial upside?

If any of these element is missing, it's likely you won't get the results you hope for.

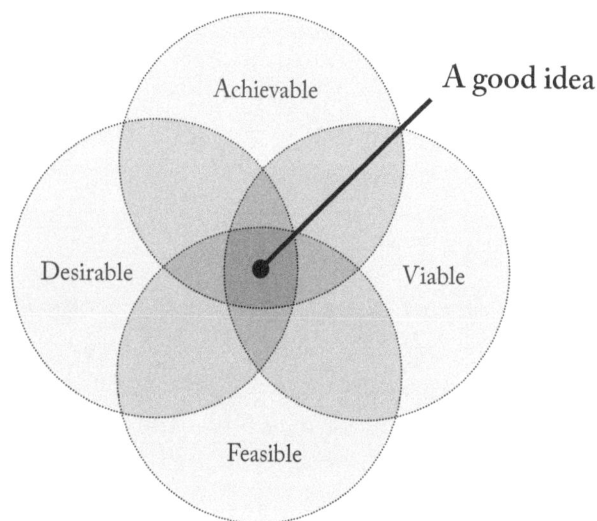

At the end of each pilot phase, we encourage you to evaluate your solution against these four criteria. In order to move to full-scale implementation, you should have very high confidence in the idea. The goal of each pilot should be to refine the idea and improve your confidence vis-à-vis these criteria. Just as with the Decision Quality chain, the quality of your idea is only as good as the weakest link. Score the idea out of 10 against each criteria:

- A score of 10 means you are absolutely certain the idea meets the criteria.
- A score of 0 means you are absolutely certain the solution does not meet the criteria.
- A score of 5 means you are completely unsure.

Scoring the quality of your idea

	Score out of 10	Give reasons/provide evidence	Strategy to test/improve
Desirable: Are you solving a real need?			
Feasible: Will your solution work as intended?			
Viable: Is it financially or operationally sustainable?			
Achievable: Can you get it done with the human and material resources available?			

Finally, do not lose sight of the reason for deploying a pilot in the first place: It is part of the learning process, so you must be willing to discard what you've created and start again if your findings do not support your concept. The purpose of the pilot process is to test assumptions, evaluate your design solutions, find points of failure, and learn from them, refine, and repeat. This is not so common in healthcare implementations, but if you hold to human-centric and data-driven principles you will ultimately arrive at solutions that are worthwhile, appropriate, and effective.

Once your idea has proven its efficacy through the Pilot phases, you can now turn, in conclusion, to how you might Spread your initiative. This is where you celebrate your progress, communicate the value of your work to your stakeholders, and move towards widespread implementation across your organization and beyond.

Spread

"The design is done when the problem goes away."

—Jason Fried

The end goal of Discovery Design is not an app, a new role, or a new process. It is a handoff that leads to continuing refinement and sustained value—in other words, to some level of cultural change. As designers, your success is measured by your ability to make others successful in the long term. Having generated, tested, piloted, and proven your concept, it's tempting to think that your work is done, but that's not the case. One more stage will carry you across the finish line and you will be ready to integrate your idea into your institution's cultural operating system.

Process steps

Step 8-1 Communicating your solution

Help your idea take root.

Step 8-2 Make the business case

Demonstrate the value created.

Step 8-3 Presenting the idea

Prepare the boardroom pitch.

Step 8-4 Spreading the wealth

Take it from pilot to policy.

Step 8-5 Bake it in

Make it the new normal.

Step 8-1 Communicating your solution

Help your idea take root.

Once your concepts have coalesced into a set of ideas that you believe are the best solutions to your challenge, you are ready to communicate your solutions for wider implementation. You'll likely need to establish a broad coalition of support before taking a request for significant funding to senior executives. Here are some suggestions for building the base.

Emphasize the strategy to address the need, not the "thing"

Nearly all solutions will include some kind of "thing"—a checklist, a widget, or a communication protocol. There is a high likelihood that people unfamiliar with your process will confuse this tangible "thing" with your solution. Be careful to emphasize the kind of experience you have created, the behaviors your solution has changed, and the system you have created; what you have created is a strategy to address a need, not a thing. Don't let your audience be distracted by details of your current implementation. "I don't like the typeface" is the last thing you want to hear.

Capture the design intent

Tell the audience what is really important about your idea from the point of view of experience. Review your design principles from Step 5-3. Use headlines—for example, "Peer-to-peer sharing," "Natural language communication of medicines," or "face-to-face connection among user groups"—that capture the design at the highest level. While the details of an idea might change, these strategic principles are where the design intent resides and are what people should refer to in future.

Tell stories

Concentrate on communicating the experience that your concepts will create. Show a situation that represents something that you saw during observations, and show the impact your solution will have. Support it with data, direct quotations, and photos of the solution in use.

Be visual

People have attended thousands of presentations, and their first reaction to a slide deck may be to pull out their smartphones and check their email. Try to distinguish your meeting from others by the way you engage the audience and the language you use. You have engaged in a creative process for this project; use that expectation to your advantage. Make sure your process is represented in the space and not just in the deck, for example, by hanging up posters with images from your observations. Create working spaces with whiteboards and posters with written questions that engage the audience. Markers and pads of sticky notes on each seat invite everyone to participate.

Be tangible

Include artifacts. If you can make the ideas feel real by producing visualizations with little effort, do so; this can help people imagine the reality of the idea and elicit helpful feedback. Examples include brochures, posters, and hand-drawn software screens. Moderate your effort accordingly. The danger of over-developing an idea is that you can become committed to it before your stakeholder team has had a chance to suggest ways of improving it.

Provide a takeaway

You want people to think about these ideas after the meeting, so leave them with a printed notebook or a set of cards with key quotes from research—something impactful that they would want to share with colleagues.

Solicit feedback

While your presentation marks the end point of the design process, it's actually the kickoff to its wider implementation. Even in this final meeting, it is important to be open-minded. It's appropriate to be strong and confident about your insights and opportunities, but let your audience know their precise form and tangible expression is still up for development.

Looking Forward

Paint a picture of what continued development of the solution might look like. Give people something to say "yes" to, rather than expecting them to figure out what should come next. This will prevent your ideas from descending into "business as usual" and getting stuck in committee. It also helps in sending the message that this is not the end of a process but the beginning of its realization.

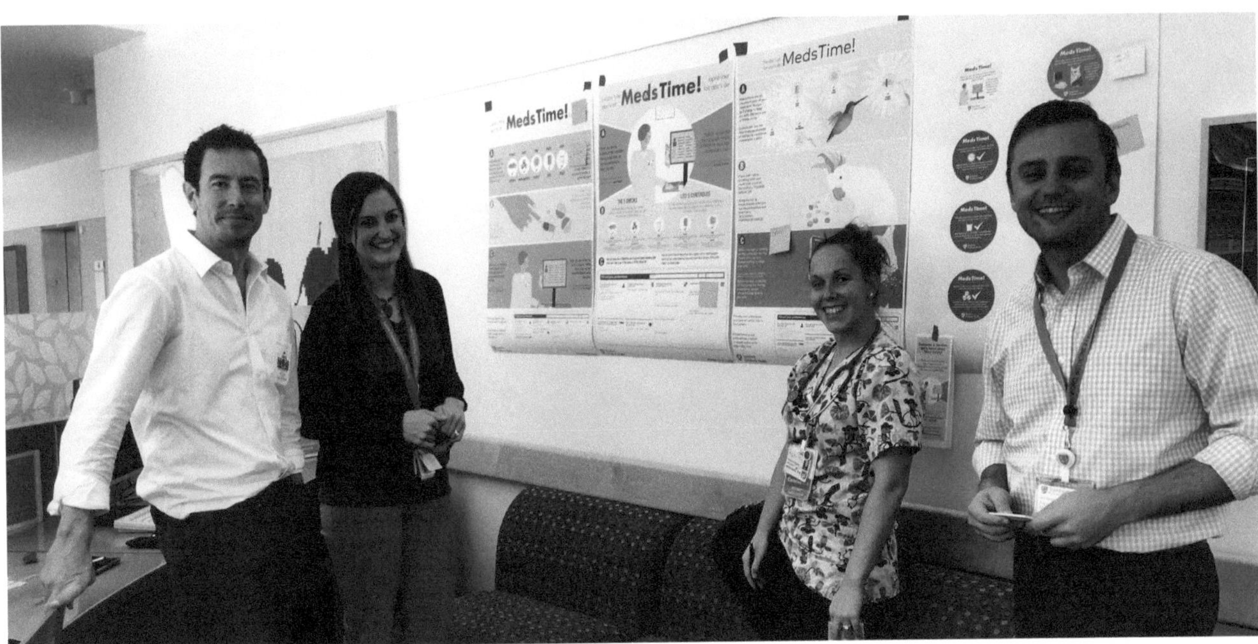

Throughout your project, take photos! Capturing key moments along the journey will create a trail that you can look back on. It will help remind others of the insights you learned, milestones you accomplished, and perhaps most importantly, the decisions that have been made along the way. In this photo, we captured a design review of various posters aimed at engaging patients and families in safety. It was a key moment in the project where the team converged on a single direction.

Step 8-2 Make the business case

Demonstrate the value created.

For your idea to be adopted and stick in the long term, you should demonstrate the value it is creating for the organization, its clinicians and staff, its patients and families, and the wider community. Ideally, your organization will have already accepted your solution and committed the necessary resources to ensuring its success. Where significant capital investment makes it necessary to choose among alternatives, however, you may need to make the business case by showing the financial return. Large investment requests are almost certain to be assessed against other organizational priorities and will have to compete for limited resources.

Net present value

A key strategy for healthcare innovators is to become familiar with your organization's capital budget processes and the thresholds they set for approving expenditures.

"Net Present Value" (NPV) is a standard approach that financial decision-makers use to determine the value of an investment opportunity, whether upgrading to new digital tools, launching a new service line, or purchasing a piece of capital equipment. NPV is a powerful tool for demonstrating returns over time.

Rather than a simple cost/benefit calculation, NPV takes into account the time value of money:

- First, $1 today is worth more than $1 tomorrow, so any investment that delivers less than the rate of inflation is losing money.
- Second, an investor should expect to receive a rate of return at least as good as what they could expect from a venture with similar risks, such as in the stock or lending markets.

NPV is calculated by translating the net return (benefits - costs) of an investment over time into today's money. The translation into today's money is done by applying a "discount rate," which represents the time value of money. Discount rates can vary widely by project and institution and over time.

$$\text{NPV} = \sum \frac{\text{Net Return for Year } n}{(1 + \text{Discount Rate})^n}$$

"n" refers to the year whose net return is being discounted.

Calculating NPV

Let's consider the example of a hospital safety program: You have identified an opportunity to save millions for your hospital by investing in a new communications tool for dispensing medications. After forecasting the various costs and benefits of the program (using the decision analysis methods we described in Phase 1), you estimate the program will save $1.5M in Year 2, $2M in Year 3, and $2.5M in Year 4, for a total of $6M. The program will cost $2M to implement in Year 1, with ongoing costs of $500k each year.

Use this procedure to calculate the Net Present Value:

1. Determine the initial investment cost (C).
2. Determine the time period (n).
3. Determine discount rate (i).
4. Estimate the costs and revenues (or savings) for each year.
5. Calculate the Discounted Costs and Revenue for each year = P/(1+i)^n).
6. Calculate the Yearly Discounted Cashflows = Discounted costs + Discounted Revenues for each year.
7. Calculate the NPV Costs = SUM(Discounted Costs).
8. Calculate the NPV Revenues = SUM(Discounted Revenues).
9. Calculate the NPV = NPV Costs + NPV Revenues.
10. Calculate the ROI = (NPV / -NPV Costs) / n.

Now, let's calculate the NPV for our example:

Initial cost (C)	-2
Time period	4 years
Discount rate	4%

YEAR	1	2	3	4
Costs	-2.00	-0.50	-0.50	-0.50
Revenues		1.50	2.00	2.50
Discounted costs	-2.00	-0.48	-0.46	-0.44
Discounted revenues	0.00	1.44	1.85	2.22
Yearly discounted cashflows	-2.00	0.96	1.39	1.78
NPV costs	-3.39			
NPV Revenue = SUM (Discounted Revenues)	5.51			
NPV = NPV costs + NPV Revenues	2.13			
ROI	16%			

Story

In 2014, 54 employees of the Stanford Hospitals were injured from slipping and falling, a trend that was contributing to financial losses as well as human suffering. Focusing on housekeepers, a task force recognized that workers' choice of footwear (slip vs. nonslip shoes) represented an opportunity to improve worker safety. They broke down the data and devised three different scenarios: The current program (none), which had a net present value of $44,000; a voluntary program in which housekeepers purchase their own shoes, with a net present value of $180,000; a program in which the hospital purchases shoes for staff and monitors the program, which had a net present value of $487,000. Based on this risk evaluation, the advantage of the third option became apparent, and all employees were fitted for two pairs of nonslip shoes in styles of their choosing. Stanford continues to monitor the effectiveness of the mandatory program, but as of August 2016, there have been no more than two injuries related to slips. Although the third option required the largest initial capital investment, decision science showed that it would yield the greatest value to the organization.

You may wish to partner with an analyst from your organization to use NPV to value your new idea.

Building on the net present value calculation, healthcare organizations, often evaluate large investments by referring to the "internal rate of return" (IRR). The IRR is determined by calculating the discount rate that makes the NPV equal to zero; the higher the IRR, the better the investment. Your organization may have set a threshold to approve or reject proposed ventures, which you'll need to be aware of. For example, if a proposed investment doesn't deliver more than a 23% IRR, it won't be considered.

You now have a reliable, quantitative basis for making the case for your initiative.

Step 8-3 Presenting your Idea

Prepare the boardroom pitch.

There is always organizational inertia to resist a new idea, and perhaps even active resistance. If your idea is to gain sufficient momentum to overcome these obstacles, you will need to be able to communicate your idea quickly, concisely, and convincingly. A compelling five-minute presentation will always be an asset. It will structure informal conversations, land in executive's inboxes, and maybe even propel your team onto the stage of a TED conference. It's an investment of time that will pay back many times over.

Your presentation should leave an audience excited about the idea and eager to be part of it. You may need to create several different variations depending on your audience, but a strong spine will make this relatively quick and easy to do.

The boardroom pitch

1. Highlight the potential

Create an evocative statement that will stoke interest in the opportunities you see. Frame it in visionary terms: "What if...?"

2. Build a narrative

Tell an evocative story of what inspired the idea and how you uncovered the underlying need. The narrative should be empathic as well as engaging: What are the priorities for these decision makers? What are they concerned about? Describe feedback received from pilots run. What can you say is working really well? Where are the opportunities? Include direct evidence of your observations and feedback sessions. Senior audiences often find it refreshing and clarifying to hear the authentic voice of the end-user, whether patients or staff.

3. Communicate the value

Why is this solution of value to the various stakeholders—and especially those to whom you are pitching? What are the costs of doing nothing? Be explicit and illustrative. Create visuals that capture the potential of the solution: the end-states and the impact. We encourage you to consider using a professional illustrator to create memorable and powerful visuals.

4. The ask

What are you asking for from your audience? What are your needs? Be explicit and specific. This part of your presentation should be modular; be ready to change it almost every time you share the presentation. You must speak directly to this audience, today. These might include: a new role or position, budget, permission or statements of support, or allocations of resources.

5. Encourage contribution

Your stakeholders will want to feel that they have delivered value to the meeting. Give them an activity (such as a feedback capture exercise) for them to deliver their thoughts and ideas. Explain how they can remain involved and updated as you launch the idea. For example, will you create a program advisory committee or board?

Step 8-4 Spreading the wealth

Take it from pilot to policy.

Who owns your idea now? Throughout the Discovery Design process, you have engaged with a subset of the people for whom this concept was created and whose lives will be affected by it. Having launched your pilot, you should now have data that supports embedding the concept into everyday practice. At this point, ownership of the new project begins to transfer from the core team to some other group. This can be an awkward moment.

Your team may no longer own the concept, but without your continued support, the chances of it being diluted, misunderstood, or even abandoned are high. It is not uncommon to find that a new idea is stalled or abandoned based on issues that might seem entirely tractable for your design team, but insuperable to people unfamiliar with the process. It's critical, therefore, to remain allied with the key organizational owners and support them in specific ways.

In the world of healthcare, there are many stakeholders whose endorsement is required before any systemic change can be fully implemented. Observing the strategy of "500 Coffees" (see Phase 2-1) will help to sustain political support and identify hidden obstacles on the road to launch, such as new competing priorities, or emerging concerns that you can anticipate. Here are some constituencies to consider:

1. Leadership

The closer to launch, and the more systemic your concept, the more visibility it is sure to get (sometimes without you present to defend it). Be proactive in understanding who will review the final implementation and at what forum. Work with your senior sponsors so that they always go into a room with a presentation or prototype that is appropriate to that audience. A little can go a long way: Creating a concise executive summary that ends in a clear recommendation will help keep a meeting on track.

The executive summary

Create a single-page Executive Summary that captures the story of the project concisely and clearly. Senior leadership probably did not attend early meetings, and may not have time to review the project background in detail. Your executive summary should:

- State what the idea achieves in a single sentence
- Say how it achieves this outcome
- Say what the idea is, including images if possible.
- Show any impact metrics possible, including quotes if relevant.

The importance of condensing the project to a single page cannot be overstated: in our present age of hundreds of emails, you'll need your project to be adequately understood by anyone in less than three minutes. Everyone can relate to the internet slang, TL;DR: ("Too long; didn't read.").

Find out their needs

- Find out what audiences executive leadership needs to convince. If leadership has to have an idea reviewed by a committee or board, find out how they wish to present and supply a presentation.
- Find out what metrics matter to them.
- Find out what initiatives they are already engaged with. If you can align your concept to existing momentum, there will be less resistance.

Be ready to flex

As a design project team, there is often much you cannot know about institutional changes that are planned or in progress or about the strong preferences of senior leadership. Remain clear on your design principles, but recognize that redesigning your concept to meet new information is nearly always a part of the journey.

Story

The leader of a psychiatric unit violence reduction project commented, "I've lost count of the number of times people have told me how they feel validated and how glad they are that someone is at last listening to them. One ward manager told me how positively her team responded when she emphasized the need for consistency with one of their chosen interventions: 'This was your idea,' she pointed out. 'You asked for it and you know how well it works.'"

2. Frontline champions

Elevating the role of frontline clinicians and other staff—not only through the idea generation process, but through implementation is powerful. Don't just "use" them for idea generation. Help them develop a sense of ownership by giving them specific tasks to help integrate the change into the organization.

3. Patient representatives

Many progressive institutions involve patients in any change that affects patient care. As designers, we should regard their input as an asset. If we can communicate the nature of the process and the sincerity of our intent, a good solution will typically receive a warm response. Be prepared to create a short summary that focuses on the process and how you incorporated direct engagements at every stage. Avoid overly technical language and focus on any potential for improved patient experience.

4. Brand and marketing

Your institution may have a group that manages its external brand and that probably has not been involved in the project from its inception (which is often the case if your project started in the technical or clinical domain). It can come as a shock to the design team to learn that there may already be standards in place regarding such things as posters, brochures and written or even spoken communications.

Rather than challenge them after the fact, the solution is to engage them as early as possible, keeping in mind that although your approaches may differ, your goals are always aligned. They, too, are professionals, and it is likely that if you respect overall brand guidelines (color, typography, terminology), your design intent will be enhanced and such deviations as you may request will be given a fair hearing.

5. Logistical support

As your team disengages from the day-to-day management of the project, progress can all too easily slide off the rails. In that case, you must be prepared to provide tactical support to parties—vendors, manufacturers, contractors—whose participation is critical, but who may be used to doing things in a certain way.

These are the institutional partners that will move your idea from prototypes to concepts to hard-wired changes that will improve the lives of patients and their families, doctors, nurses, and pharmacists, hospital administrators and staff, and the entire range of participants and beneficiaries. Your work is not done, but you should be proud of your accomplishment.

Step 8-5 Bake it in

Make it the new normal.

If the ongoing success of a program relies on a particular person it is not likely to be stable or sustainable over time. It needs to become part of the "new normal," baked into the infrastructure of the institution.

New solutions need to stand on their own without the need for the constant advocacy of a few motivated individuals. In order to hold the gains you have made, consider the following strategies:

1. **Make it concrete.**

Solutions should find their home in policies, budgets, job descriptions, and strategic deployment plans. Be sure to document the underlying rationale, processes, and requirements behind the solution. A flowchart of a process map can be used as a reference point if the team needs to revisit any aspect of the solution.

2. **Monitor and refine.**

"Sustainable" does not mean "autopilot!" Solutions need a mechanism for periodic evaluation and refinement, and you will need to determine who will be responsible for that. Involve frontline stakeholders to set up systems for accountability and continuous improvement, not just to the specific solution but also to your learning about improving design strategies. Encourage them to bring forward any gaps in knowledge, skills, systems, or processes, and empower them in refining the program.

3. **Celebrate the benefits!**

Agree on realistic goals and evaluation criteria for 6 or 12 months down the track. This may involve systematic and continuous collection of data and its dissemination at many levels of the organization so that the value of the solution is understood and felt by staff and leaders. Create a communications plan for sharing the benefits of the solution with patients, staff, clinicians, and the organization on an ongoing basis.

4. **Make it adaptable.**

Healthcare organizations are always changing. In some of our projects, key partners were promoted because of their good work—but before the project had completed! Can the solution withstand organizational and personnel changes and internal pressures? What if a key funding source, stakeholder, technology, or vendor is removed? How might you make it immune to these stressors? What kinds of redundancies can you put in place?

5. Enable succession.

Eventually, you will need to deliver the project into the care of another person or group. You will probably be unaware of the institutional knowledge you have developed and the impact of your presence on the success of the solution. Before that time comes, consider: How might you set up the new custodians for success? Who are the key players and stakeholders they can rely on? What observations, insights, prototypes, and pilots brought the solution to life? What were the key stories, reasons, or numbers that made implementation possible? What's the one thing others should know in order to be successful?

> "The challenge is not starting, but continuing after the initial enthusiasm has gone."
>
> —John Øvretveit

The Big Finish!

"You're off to Great Places!
Today is your day!
Your mountain is waiting,
So... get on your way!
- Oh, the Places You'll Go!"
—Dr. Seuss

Conclusion

From possibilities to policy

You have now completed a journey that has carried you from discovering unmet needs within your organization, reframing them as opportunities, and translating them into new products, processes, or policies. Along the way, you have covered acres of wall space with colorful sticky notes, learned that it's possible to build a prototype of pretty much anything, made a lot of new friends, and quite possibly a few enemies. Don't worry about them—they'll get over it once they see what you've accomplished.

As you move from the stealth of your project space out into the open, your energy and commitment will probably have begun to attract the attention of other would-be innovators. You can use your hard-won recognition to inspire them, just as we, at The Risk Authority and Future Medical Systems, have sought to inspire you. Your example proves that change is possible, even in the complex, high-stakes world of healthcare.

In this sense, the last stage in the Discovery Design process is really the first stage of what follows, namely sharing your solutions—and the process that enabled you to achieve them. Start small: unit, department, institution to broader horizons and even the healthcare industry at large. You are poised to turn from innovator to ambassador.

To be sure, no formula can be generalized to every situation; the healthcare environment is far too complex and its organizations too varied in scale and specialty. It is nonetheless worth considering how the solutions you have worked so hard to create might be adapted to the specific needs, culture, and processes of your counterparts at other organizations. Moreover, you will find that there are some tangible advantages to doing so.

At The Risk Authority's Communication and Resolution program, "PEARL," we're often approached by other organizations hoping to embark on patient-centered programs of their own. What we discovered is that although our process worked well for us, there were unwritten codes and troves of accumulated wisdom that were integral to its success. It was only in the process of implementing Discovery Design at another hospital that we were challenged to identify those underlying principles, revisit our assumptions, and refine our processes. In the course of implementing our solutions elsewhere, we found more efficient and effective ways of using them at home.

In the same spirit, the victories you have worked so hard to achieve deserve to be shared with the world. How might you "productize" your solutions so that others can benefit from what you have learned? Speaking at conferences? Submitting your design for awards? Writing papers for popular, professional, or peer-reviewed journals? Congratulate yourselves on your success, but keep pushing the envelope. Remember that the key to the designer's mindset is optimism—the belief that no initiative that measurably improves the lives of patients and the professionals who serve them is too big or too small.

In that spirit, we encourage you to report back to us: What worked? What didn't? Tell us how you used the Discovery Design Handbook, and how we might improve upon it. We would love to hear from you.

Tag us on Twitter at #DiscoveryDesign

Visit our website, where you'll find opportunities for collaboration, storytelling, additional resources, and templates: www.discoverydesign.healthcare

You can contact The Risk Authority at riskmanagement@stanfordhealthcare.org and Future Medical Systems at hello@futuremedicalsystems.com

Bibliography and Resources

Discovery Design draws upon the literature of design thinking, ergonomics and human factors, quality improvement, risk management, and decision analysis. In addition to specific material referenced in the handbook, we offer here a selection of books, articles, papers, courses, and blogs that have inspired our thinking and shaped our methods. We hope you can use this as a library as you tackle the most important challenges facing your patients, providers, communities, and healthcare organizations.

Bibliography

Boston-Fleischhauer, Carol. 2008. "Enhancing Healthcare Process Design with Human Factors Engineering and Reliability Science, Part 1: Setting the Context." The Journal of Nursing Administration 38 (1): 27–32.

Buchanan, Leigh. 2016. "The Most Productive Teams at Google Have These 5 Dynamics." Inc.com. Inc. April 12. https://www.inc.com/leigh-buchanan/most-productive-teams-at-google.html.

Denzin, NK., Lincoln, YS. 2017. The SAGE Handbook of Qualitative Research. SAGE Publications.

Kahneman, David. 2011. Thinking, Fast and Slow. Farrar, Straus and Giroux.

Knowles, Malcolm. 1980. The Modern Practice of Adult Education: From Pedagogy to Andragogy. Association Press.

McNamee, P., Celona, J. 2001. Decision Analysis for the Professional. SmartOrg.

Nael, M., O. Bobjer, H. McLoone, J. K. Kwahk, W. Friesdorf, S. Glende, and R. Bruder. 2008. "EQUID (Ergonomic Quality In Design) Design Process Guidelines: Requirements for Ergonomic Quality Management in the Design Process for Products and Services." International Ergonomics Association.

Nolan, T., Resar, R., Griffin, F., Gordon, AB. 2004. "Improving the Reliability of Health Care." Innovation Series. Institute for Healthcare Improvement.

Rodriguez, HP., Meredith, LS., Hamilton, AB., Yano, E.M., Rubenstein, LV. 2015. "Huddle up!: The Adoption and Use of Structured Team Communication for VA Medical Home Implementation." Health Care Management Review 40 (4): 286–99.

Sharek, Paul J., Jeffrey D. Horbar, Wilbert Mason, Hema Bisarya, Cary W. Thurm, Gautham Suresh, James E. Gray, William H. Edwards, Donald Goldmann, and David Classen. 2006. "Adverse Events in the Neonatal Intensive Care Unit: Development, Testing, and Findings of an NICU-Focused Trigger Tool to Identify Harm in North American NICUs." Pediatrics 118 (4): 1332–40.

Solberg, LI., Mosser, G., and McDonald, S. 1997. "The Three Faces of Performance Measurement: Improvement, Accountability, and Research." The Joint Commission Journal on Quality Improvement 23 (3): 135–47.

Vincent, C., Young, M., Phillips, A. 1994. "Why Do People Sue Doctors? A Study of Patients and Relatives Taking Legal Action." The Lancet 343 (8913): 1609–13.

Westbrook JI., Woods, A., Rob, MI., Dunsmuir, WTM., Day, RO. "Association of Interruptions with an Increased Risk and Severity of Medication Administration Errors." Arch Intern Med. 2010;170(8):683–690.

Wolf, ZR., Hughes, RG. 2011. "Error Reporting and Disclosure." In Patient Safety and Quality: An Evidence-Based Handbook for Nurses, edited by Ronda G. Hughes. Rockville (MD): Agency for Healthcare Research and Quality (US).

Recommended Further Reading

Brown, Tim. 2008. "Design Thinking." Harvard Business Review 86 (6): 84–92, 141.

Brown, Tim, and B. Katz. 2009. Change by Design: How Design Thinking Transforms Organizations and Inspires Innovation. Harper Collins.

Celona, J., J. Driver, and E. Hall. 2011. "Value-driven ERM: Making ERM an Engine for Simultaneous Value Creation and Value Protection." Journal of Healthcare Risk Management: The Journal of the American Society for Healthcare Risk Management.

Driver, J. F., and K. Driver, eds. 2017. RiskScape. The Risk Authority.

Duhigg, Charles. 2016. "What Google Learned From Its Quest to Build the Perfect Team." The New York Times, February 25. https://www.nytimes.com/2016/02/28/magazine/what-google-learned-from-its-quest-to-build-the-perfect-team.html.

Geller, SE. 2016. The Psychology of Safety Handbook. CRC Press.

Goodwin, Kim. 2011. Designing for the Digital Age: How to Create Human-Centered Products and Services. John Wiley & Sons.

Hanington, Bruce, and Bella Martin. 2012. Universal Methods of Design: 100 Ways to Research Complex Problems, Develop Innovative Ideas, and Design Effective Solutions. Rockport Publishers.

Holton-Burke, R. C., and D. S. Buck. 2017. "Social Interventions Can Lower Costs and Improve Outcomes - NEJM Catalyst." NEJM Catalyst. March 7. https://catalyst.nejm.org/social-interventions-improve-outcomes/.

Katz, Barry M. 2015. Make It New: A History of Silicon Valley Design. MIT Press.

Kelley, Tom, and David Kelley. 2013. Creative Confidence: Unleashing the Creative Potential Within Us All. Crown Publishing Group.

Kolko, Jon. 2011. Exposing the Magic of Design: A Practitioner's Guide to the Methods and Theory of Synthesis. Oxford University Press.

Langley, Gerald J., Ronald D. Moen, Kevin M. Nolan, Thomas W. Nolan, Clifford L. Norman, and Lloyd P. Provost. 2009. The Improvement Guide: A Practical Approach to Enhancing Organizational Performance. John Wiley & Sons.

Lin, M., B. Hughes, M. Katica, C. Zuber, and P. Plsek. 2011. "Service Design and Change of Systems: Human-Centered Approaches to Implementing and Spreading Service Design." International Journal of Design 5 (2).

Martin, Roger L., and Christensen, K. 2013. Rotman on Design: The Best on Design Thinking from Rotman Magazine. University of Toronto Press.

Martin, Roger L. 2009. The Design of Business: Why Design Thinking Is the Next Competitive Advantage. Harvard Business Press.

McCreary, L. 2010. "Kaiser Permanente's Innovation on the Front Lines." Harvard Business Review. September 1. https://hbr.org/2010/09/kaiser-permanentes-innovation-on-the-front-lines.

Mooallem, J. 2015. "Death, Redesigned." The California Sunday Magazine. April 5. https://stories.californiasunday.com/2015-04-05/death-redesigned.

Norman, Don. 2013. The Design of Everyday Things: Revised and Expanded Edition. Basic Books.

Roberts, Jess P., Thomas R. Fisher, Matthew J. Trowbridge, and Christine Bent. 2016. "A Design Thinking Framework for Healthcare Management and Innovation." Healthcare (Amsterdam, Netherlands) 4 (1): 11–14.

Roller, Margaret R., and Paul J. Lavrakas. 2015. Applied Qualitative Research Design: A Total Quality Framework Approach. Guilford Publications.

Sarpatwari, R. 2015. "Better Health, By Design." Footnote. July 17. http://footnote.co/better-health-by-design/

Sutton, R. I., and H. Rao. 2016. Scaling up Excellence: Getting to More without Settling for Less. Random House.

Online Learning

The Stanford D. School Virtual Crash Course in Design

IDEO + Acumen Design Kit for Human Centered Design

Stanford Certificate in Innovation & Entrepreneurship

Institute of Healthcare Improvement Basic Certificate in Quality and Safety

Strategic Decisions & Risk Management Certificate

Blogs

Design Thinking by Tim Brown
designthinking.ideo.com

DesignMind by frog design
designmind.frogdesign.com

HyperObservant by Future Medical Systems
hyperobservant.tumblr.com

MakerNurse
makernurse.com

NEJM Catalyst
catalyst.nejm.org

Stanford Medicine X
medicinex.stanford.edu/blog

The Risk Authority
theriskauthority.com/blog

IRB
RX

Lightning Source UK Ltd.
Milton Keynes UK
UKHW050534091020
371274UK00003BA/83